A Declarer's Workbook

Gene Simpson

and

Al Wilson

Published by Arbor Crest Publishing

ISBN 978-0-9796746-5-5

♠ ♥ ♣ ♦ ♠

To all of the people in the bridge world that I am lucky enough to call my friends. Without you it would just be counting to 52.

Gene Simpson

To my parents, Albert and Janet Wilson, and to my loving wife, Genevieve.

In addition to giving me an education, love and support my parents introduced me to the wonderful game of Bridge. For everything, I thank you.

Genevieve came into my life in 2011. I have come to know happiness and contentment that I never knew was possible. Her patience and encouragement while Gene and I worked on this book was invaluable. Thank you, my love.

Al Wilson

Acknowledgements

Both of us thank our spouses, Laura Kenney and Genevieve Wilson, for their patience and understanding in dealing with two authors struggling through the creative process and for their invaluable assistance in helping to edit this work. Truly, we could not have done it without you.

We also thank Claudia Kemper, Jim Griffin and Crispin Barrere for their help in editing and reviewing the problems. Your perspectives were always helpful.

Table of Contents

Introduction

This is a workbook for improving declarers. There are a number of very good texts on declarer play so what does this workbook add to the literature? Declarer faces two challenges in each hand: (1) diagnosing the hand's challenges and opportunities and (2) executing a plan that will maximize those opportunities. The existing library of declarer texts does an excellent job of teaching the techniques but they do not fully exercise an improving player's diagnostic skills.

Consider what a reader finds in a good declarer text. At the end of the chapter on combining plays the reader will encounter 8 or 10 excellent problems on that subject. Learning how to execute the combining play is one thing. Learning how to recognize the opportunity is quite another. At the table a declarer does not have the luxury of the hint provided in the text book − that all of the problems at the end of a given chapter involve that chapter's subject. Our experience playing with and against improving players tells us that many have trouble recognizing the challenges and opportunities before them. This workbook addresses that weakness. It is intended to help the reader become better at identifying challenges to their contract and then designing and executing the optimum solution.

We have divided this workbook into two sections. In the first we introduce each of the topics including a straightforward problem or two. In the second section we shuffle the problems by subject so that the reader has no hint what challenges the next problem presents. We are trying to duplicate what each declarer faces at the table. Every good declarer has excellent diagnostic skills. One purpose of this book is to help the reader acquire those skills. Each of the problems contains a challenge. The reader's task is to find out what the challenge is and to design the best solution for it. Just as in real life, many of the problems, especially those appearing later in the book, involve multiple challenges and require more intricate solutions.

We have presented over 100 problems on 13 subjects. Our hope is that the reader will work through the book and then rework the problems a number of times. Gaining diagnostic skills requires practice and that is what this workbook provides. Just as with an athlete, we believe that repeating an exercise can help improve performance in competition.

Each problem description includes all of the bidding and early play. Unless stated otherwise East/West are using standard leads and signals. Where necessary we have adjusted the bidding to conform to modern systems – usually Two Over One but sometimes Standard American. We have not used other bidding systems because we want to concentrate on declarer play, not bidding, and we want to use bidding that all players understand. Sometimes the auctions are less than ideal but there are no clear gaffes. We readily admit that some of the auctions are less than expert. What you will see is a reasonable if not ideal way of reaching the contract that presents the challenges that we want the improving player to identify and solve.

Section One

Introducing the Topics

Probability Split Table

Number of Cards Held By Opponents	Split	Probability %
7	4–3	62
	5–2	31
	6–1	7
	7–0	<0.5
6	4–2	48
	3–3	36
	5–1	15
	6–0	1
5	3–2	68
	4–1	28
	5–0	4
4	3–1	50
	2–2	40
	4–0	10
3	2–1	78
	3–0	22
2	1–1	52
	2–0	48

Avoidance Plays

All bridge players have experienced having Kx(xx) in one hand facing xx(xx) in the other. We know that one defender is not nearly as dangerous as the other because a lead through our King is a far greater threat than a lead up to our King. This and similar situations lead to the concept of the "dangerous hand." Keeping the dangerous hand off lead often takes precedence over other considerations when devising the best strategy for playing a hand. In bridge terminology this topic is usually referred to as an Avoidance Play – keeping the dangerous hand off of the lead. We are going to present a series of problems requiring avoidance plays. We need to develop the skill to recognize the need for an avoidance play and the additional skill to create a strategy for executing one.

North
- ♠ 964
- ♥ K105
- ♦ KJ95
- ♣ KQ4

Vul: Both; Dealer: East

East	*South*	*West*	*North*
P	1♥	P	2♦[1]
P	3♦	P	4♥
All Pass			

South
- ♠ K7
- ♥ AJ963
- ♦ AQ3
- ♣ 862

1. Game forcing with Diamonds.

Lead: ♦2 (Standard leads). Plan the play.

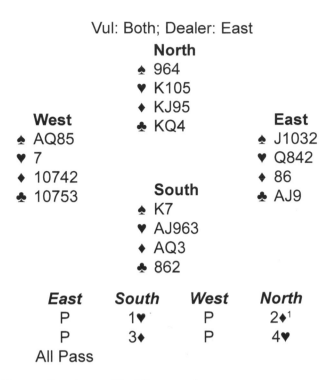

Vul: Both; Dealer: East

North
♠ 964
♥ K105
♦ KJ95
♣ KQ4

West
♠ AQ85
♥ 7
♦ 10742
♣ 10753

East
♠ J1032
♥ Q842
♦ 86
♣ AJ9

South
♠ K7
♥ AJ963
♦ AQ3
♣ 862

East	South	West	North
P	1♥	P	2♦[1]
P	3♦	P	4♥
All Pass			

1. Game forcing with Diamonds.

Lead: ♦2 (Standard leads). Plan the play.

You start with 5 possible losers. One loser can go on the fourth Diamond after drawing trump. A finesse in Hearts is right but which way? What if the finesse loses? If East wins then you could get a Spade lead and two Spade losers could ensue. If you finesse the other way and it loses, West cannot win two Spade tricks by attacking Spades. This approach has the additional benefit of protecting you from a 4–1 trump split but the primary concern is avoiding a Spade lead from East. On this layout your approach works beautifully. After drawing trump you should immediately play four Diamond tricks, pitching either a Spade or Club from your hand. Doing so guarantees your contract since the trump finesse won.. If the trump finesse had lost you would be under pressure. If the ♣A and ♠A were both unfavorably located you might go down but you would have done all that you could. But if West held the ♣A you would be safe regardless of where the ♠A was located. Not so if you took the trump finesse the other way and it lost.

A Declarer's Workbook

2

Combining Your Chances

On this hand the bidding and opening lead are normal. East plays the
♠J. You win your ♠K.

North
- ♠ 983
- ♥ K95
- ♦ A754
- ♣ A85

Vul: Both; Dealer: East

East	South	West	North
P	1NT	P	3NT
All Pass			

Lead: ♠7 (standard leads).

South
- ♠ K6
- ♥ AJ7
- ♦ KJ86
- ♣ KQ64

Counting the Spade trick you have eight winners so you need one
more. On first glance it looks like you have to choose between
finesses in either red suit or hoping for a 3–3 split in Clubs. One
thing is sure: if you lose the lead the Opponents are going to cash a
lot of Spade tricks.

You know little about the Opponents' hands so it looks like the
finesses each have a 50% chance. You also know that your seven
card Club suit will usually not divide 3–3 (the actual chance is 36%).
Since a finesse has a better chance than 3–3 Clubs it might seem that
you should flip a mental coin to guess which red suit finesse to take.
There is a better way. Combine your chances.

You can play to the top 3 Clubs to see if they break 3–3. They probably will not but if they do, you have made your contract without
having to try a finesse. Even if Clubs do not split, you still have the
lead so you can take one of the finesses. If Clubs split 3–3 you got
lucky, but there was no risk in testing the waters.

What you have done is create a situation where TWO bad things
have to happen for you to fail, not just ONE. The chance of the
finesse losing is 50%. The chance of Clubs not being 3–3 is 64%.

BOTH of these bad things will happen less than 1/3 of the time. By testing the Clubs you have improved your chance of success from 1 out of 2 to more than 2 chances out of 3. That is good but there is another chance!!

You have eight Diamonds so the Opponents have five. On some hands the ♦Q will be singleton or doubleton. Most of the time it will not but sometimes it will. If you play your ♦A and ♦K, the lady will fall about 1/3 of the time and you will have made your contract without having to take a finesse. What is vitally important is that if the ♦Q does not make an appearance you can still try the Heart finesse because you still have the lead.

By testing the Clubs and the Diamonds *before* taking the Heart finesse you have created a situation where THREE things have to fail for your contract to go down: the Clubs have to split 4–2 or worse, the ♦Q has to fail to drop in two rounds and the Heart finesse has to fail. The chance of all three of those things happening is less than 1 out of 4. That means your chances of success are now better than 3 out of 4. What looked like a pretty sketchy game has turned into a strong favorite by combining your chances *even though two of those chances succeed less than half of the time.* All of your game contracts should be this good!! Expect this concept to arise repeatedly in the hands that follow.

A Declarer's Workbook

Ruffing in the Short Hand

One of the most common opportunities to take additional tricks is by ruffing in the hand that is short in trumps. This example shows just two suits: Hearts, which are trump, and Diamonds. We will ignore the other suits and the bidding. Assume that South has the lead.

North
♥ Q72
♦ K9

South
♥ AK984
♦ A87

If you draw trump immediately and they are 3–2 you will score 5 Hearts and 2 Diamonds for a total of 7 but have 1 Diamond loser. Instead, assuming you have an entry to your hand in a black suit, draw 2 rounds of trump with the ♥Q and ♥A, play the ♦K, the ♦A and ruff a Diamond. Then come to your hand to draw the last trump. You will win 8 tricks in Diamonds and Hearts instead of 7.

If you do not have a safe entry to your hand in the black suits then you can play three rounds of Diamonds before drawing trump. The chance of a Diamond getting ruffed is minimal but a Diamond loser is certain if you do not ruff it before drawing all of the trump.

The vital point is that you have scored an extra trick by ruffing that third Diamond. Where did it come from? The difference is that Dummy's ♥2 took a trick instead of falling under the ♥A when drawing trump. After the ♥2 wins you draw the remaining trump so the 5 Hearts in your hand will still score 5 tricks along with the ♥2, ♦A and ♦K for a total of 8.

There is a slim chance that a Diamond could be ruffed but the defense has 8 Diamonds. If either the first or second Diamond is ruffed then someone had 7 or 8 Diamonds and they surely would have bid them. If Diamonds are 6–2 and your ♥2 gets overruffed then you have lost nothing – you were going to lose that trick anyway and the person ruffing the Diamond might hold 4 trump and be ruffing with a natural trump trick. You can reduce the chance of an Opponent ruffing by winning the ♥Q and ♥A before playing Diamonds provided you have a safe entry back to your hand. Most importantly, be sure to get that Diamond ruff in Dummy before drawing the last trump.

Sometimes the risk of an overruff is necessary because you need that extra trick to make the contract. In a matchpoint game a possible overtrick that involves a minimal risk is usually well worth taking. We will discuss that topic in some of the coming problems.

Keep the previous example in mind while we consider another.

North
♥ Q72
♦ K97

South
♥ AK984
♦ A8

One thing has changed. Now the Diamond shortness is in the "long hand." Do we gain a trick by ruffing in the long hand before drawing trump? If we play the ♦A and the ♦K and then ruff a Diamond we will only score 4 Hearts after we draw trump. We do *not* gain a trick.

In general, ruffing in the long hand does not create tricks. There is an important exception where we ruff several times in the "long" hand until it becomes the "short" hand. We will cover that in detail in a chapter entitled "Dummy Reversal." Usually ruffing only once or twice in the long hand does not create a trick. It might be necessary to keep the opponents from winning a trick in a side suit. It also might be necessary for transportation to the long hand in order to cash some winners. Do not confuse those valuable uses of trump with ruffing in the short hand. With those two exceptions, ruffing in the "long" hand is almost never right.

Ruffing in the "short" hand usually does create tricks. Some problems that use that technique lie ahead.

Ducking to Sever Communications

When we start to play bridge we learn to take tricks. We quickly find out that the more tricks your partnership takes the better your score will be. It is easy for a novice to conclude that taking every available trick as soon as possible is a winning strategy. Sometimes that is true but often it is not. Sometimes winning the trick later is necessary for maximizing our results.

Often we need to defer taking a trick to sever communication between the Opponents. The first challenge is recognizing the need to duck a trick or two. The second challenge is figuring out how many times to duck. These problems arise most often in No Trump because you do not have trump to prevent an Opponent from running a long suit.

Consider this very common type of problem.

North
- ♠ J10
- ♥ J1073
- ♦ KQ42
- ♣ A92

Vul: None; Dealer: South

South	West	North	East
1NT	P	2♣	X
2♦¹	P	3NT²	All Pass

1. No four card major
2. Game values.

South
- ♠ AQ3
- ♥ A62
- ♦ AJ1063
- ♣ 73

Lead: ♣5. East/West are using standard signals. Plan the play.

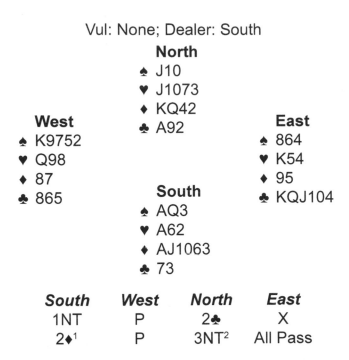

Vul: None; Dealer: South

North
- ♠ J10
- ♥ J1073
- ♦ KQ42
- ♣ A92

West
- ♠ K9752
- ♥ Q98
- ♦ 87
- ♣ 865

East
- ♠ 864
- ♥ K54
- ♦ 95
- ♣ KQJ104

South
- ♠ AQ3
- ♥ A62
- ♦ AJ1063
- ♣ 73

South	West	North	East
1NT	P	2♣	X
2♦[1]	P	3NT[2]	All Pass

1. *No four card major.*
2. *Game values.*

Lead: ♣5. East/West are using standard signals. Plan the play.

You have 8 top tricks. The Spade finesse will establish trick 9 and, if the ♠K is onside, 10 easy tricks are yours. Do you see possible disaster looming? West's ♣5 is a low one. Given East's suggestion of a Club lead West would have led high with an even number so the ♣5 probably indicates an odd number of Clubs, either 1 or 3. If it is 3 that leaves 5 Clubs with East. If the Spade finesse loses then West will surely lead another Club and East will cash the remaining 4 Club tricks, setting you by 1 trick. How can you defend against this outcome? Notice that North also has 3 Clubs. If you duck the first Club trick East will win and surely continue Clubs. Duck again. When North's ♣A wins trick 3 West will be out of Clubs. If the Spade finesse loses, West will not be able to lead a Club. You win any other return and cash you winners: 2 Spades, 1 Heart, 5 Diamonds and the ♣A. Holding up on the ♣A severed the defense's lines of communication. Expect similar problems ahead.

Crossruffs

Crossruff hands have two things in common: trump length and shortness in both hands with the shortness being in two different suits. This configuration allows declarer to use trumps one at a time, winning a trick by ruffing first in one hand and then in the other while the opponents are left to gnash their teeth. A large number of trumps divided relatively equally between Declarer and Dummy can sometimes be turned into a large number of tricks with minimal use of high cards. Here is a good example.

North
- ♠ Q832
- ♥ A1093
- ♦ 7
- ♣ J963

South
- ♠ —
- ♥ KQJ874
- ♦ 10642
- ♣ A84

Vul: None; Dealer: North

North	East	South	West
P	1♠	2♥	3♥[1]
5♥	X	All Pass	

1. *Limit raise or better in Spades.*

Lead: ♠4. Plan the play.

N/S hold 10 Hearts including all of the high ones. North is short in Diamonds and should recognize from the bidding and counting Spades that South has at most 1. Lots of trump in both hands and short suits in each hand point to a successful crossruff. Even though N/S hold only 17 HCP they cannot be prevented from taking 10 tricks in a Heart contract once West leads a Spade. Before turning the page to see all four hands we ask the reader to consider how the play should go after the ♠4 lead.

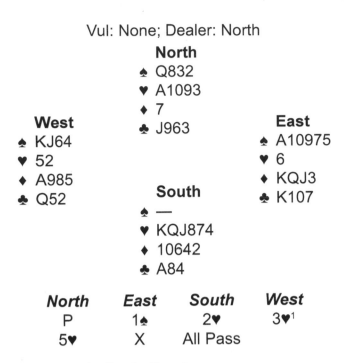

Vul: None; Dealer: North

North
- ♠ Q832
- ♥ A1093
- ♦ 7
- ♣ J963

West
- ♠ KJ64
- ♥ 52
- ♦ A985
- ♣ Q52

East
- ♠ A10975
- ♥ 6
- ♦ KQJ3
- ♣ K107

South
- ♠ —
- ♥ KQJ874
- ♦ 10642
- ♣ A84

North	*East*	*South*	*West*
P	1♠	2♥	3♥[1]
5♥	X	All Pass	

1. *Limit raise or better in Spades.*

Lead: ♠4. Plan the play.

After West's ♠4 lead South has 10 tricks. Ruff the Spade and lead a low Diamond. Even if the Opponents return a trump Declarer will be able to win the ♣A and crossruff Diamonds and Spades. Declarer will win three trump in Dummy, six trump in hand plus the ♣A. Down one for –100 is a great sacrifice against East–West's 4♠ that is worth 420. Notice the good supply of trump in each hand plus shortness in separate suits. Upon hearing about East/West's Spade fit North should know that South is short in Spades. Since North is short in Diamonds with four trumps the crossruff possibilities are clear. Before making a sacrifice bid think about the crossruffing possibilities. If you cannot visualize a crossruff do not make the bid. It is worth noting that best defense on this hand starts with a Heart lead. This reduces Declarer's ruffing power by taking two trumps out of play. If West follows this up by leading the ♥5 after winning the ♦A Declarer will only be able to ruff 2 Diamonds in Dummy. The result will be down two for –300; still a good sacrifice for North/South but a far better result for East/West than down one.

Weak Trump Suit

Sometimes we land in a contract with a very weak trump suit. We are not referring to trump length but strength. We could have Axxx facing xxxx. We have the desired 8 card fit and we have the combined high card strength for our contract. The problem is that sometimes our high card strength is in side suits, sometimes with concentrations in relatively short suits. We could easily lose control of our trump suit with the result that the Opponents might draw our trump when we had better uses for them.

Timing will be crucial. We need to maintain control over when and how trumps are played. In the example in the previous paragraph the only controlling card we have is the Ace. We need to be careful when we play that card. We are going to introduce this topic with a basic hand and then include similar, though more challenging problems.

North
- ♠ A9
- ♥ A874
- ♦ K76
- ♣ K853

Vul: Both; Dealer: South

South	West	North	East
P	P	1♣	P
1♥	P	2♥	P
4♥	All Pass		

South
- ♠ K854
- ♥ 9532
- ♦ A84
- ♣ A6

Lead: ♦J. Plan the play.

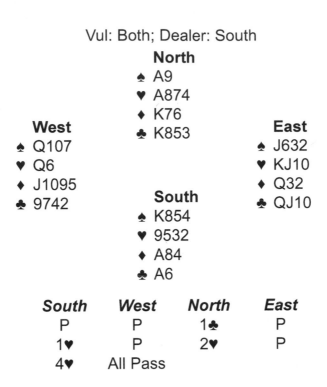

Vul: Both; Dealer: South

North
♠ A9
♥ A874
♦ K76
♣ K853

West
♠ Q107
♥ Q6
♦ J1095
♣ 9742

East
♠ J632
♥ KJ10
♦ Q32
♣ QJ10

South
♠ K854
♥ 9532
♦ A84
♣ A6

South	West	North	East
P	P	1♣	P
1♥	P	2♥	P
4♥	All Pass		

Lead: ♦J. Plan the play.

We have 25 HCP so game is appropriate. If the Opponents' hands are as balanced as ours we have 10 tricks by cross-ruffing Clubs and Spades. We need to draw two rounds of trump to prevent more than one overruff but care is needed. If we play the ♥A followed by a low Heart then the Opponent taking the second trump might lead a third trump, drawing two of ours. The solution is clear if we repress our instinctive avoidance of losing trump tricks. If we first lead a low trump and win the second with our Ace we maintain control. If trump divides 3–2 a defender will be left with a high trump but will be forced to play it when we want him to, not when they want to. We should win the ♦A, concede a low trump, win any return and play the ♥A, leaving one trump at large. We win our ♦K and then play two rounds each of Clubs and Spades. We then cross ruff those suits. The Opponent with the high trump can ruff at any time but we will still capture 10 tricks. The key is that the Opponent with the third trump was not able to draw two of our trump. If neither Opponent has a singleton in a side suit the contract will succeed.

Eight Ever, Nine Never

One of the most common problems facing a declarer is finding a missing Queen. Should you play the Ace and King and hope that the lady drops or should you take a finesse? Years ago mathematicians calculated the probabilities of success for eight card and nine card holdings assuming the defense's cards are distributed randomly.

When holding eight cards the odds definitely favor a finesse but with nine cards the odds slightly favor playing for the drop. This finding led to the oft-repeated dictum: "Eight Ever, Nine Never." The odds of dropping the Queen by playing the Ace and King are about 33% when holding eight cards but about 52% when holding nine cards. A 50% finesse is therefore better when holding eight cards but just slightly inferior when holding nine cards.

Knowledge of the Opponents' distribution or considerations of the play of the other suits often far outweigh the advantage of Eight Ever, Nine Never. We will present a series of hands where the rule should be followed and others where it should not. It is important for improving declarers to learn how to recognize the difference.

North
- ♠ K1042
- ♥ 85
- ♦ KQ2
- ♣ KQ43

Vul: Both; Dealer: West

West	North	East	South
P	1♣	P	1♠
P	2♠	P	4♠
All Pass			

South
- ♠ AJ853
- ♥ A4
- ♦ J64
- ♣ J102

Lead: ♥K. Plan the play.

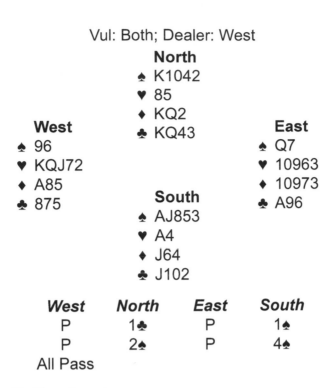

Vul: Both; Dealer: West

North
♠ K1042
♥ 85
♦ KQ2
♣ KQ43

West
♠ 96
♥ KQJ72
♦ A85
♣ 875

East
♠ Q7
♥ 10963
♦ 10973
♣ A96

South
♠ AJ853
♥ A4
♦ J64
♣ J102

West	North	East	South
P	1♣	P	1♠
P	2♠	P	4♠
All Pass			

Lead: ♥K. Plan the play.

You start with three losers: one each in Hearts, Diamonds and Clubs. You must find the ♠Q. Should you rely on "Eight Ever, Nine Never?" East and West were silent during the auction. Note further that neither Opponent is more dangerous than the other should they gain control with the ♠Q. There is no advantage to playing one Opponent for the Queen. This is a situation where "Eight Ever, Nine Ever" applies. Declarer, holding nine Spades, should play for the drop by winning the ♥A and winning two Spade tricks with the Ace and King. 52% of the time the ♠Q will fall on either the first or second round. The chance of the finesse winning is 50%. There is a small but worthwhile advantage in playing for the drop. One thing to be careful of is a 4–0 split in Spades (a 5% chance). On these cards you cannot survive 4 Spades with West but you can with East. Therefore, the correct play is to lead up to the ♠K. If West shows out you lead the ♠10 forcing East to cover. Return to Dummy with Diamonds to lead up to the ♠J–8. As long as East does not have a singleton Diamond you will make your contract. Always ask yourself if there is anything you can do about a bad split and play accordingly. Doing so will sometimes pay off big time.

A Declarer's Workbook

Taking Advantage of Shortness

Early in each person's bridge career they learn the awesome power of a good trump suit combined with shortness. All of a sudden the Opponents' Aces, Kings and Queens take on the value of twos and threes. All bridge players know that you can use trump to keep Opponents from taking tricks in their suit. Did you know that you can use trump and shortness to create tricks? We are going to present a number of hands that will show you how you can use shortness and trump in ways that you might not be aware of.

North
- ♠ AQ3
- ♥ AQ8653
- ♦ —
- ♣ QJ104

South
- ♠ 654
- ♥ KJ4
- ♦ KJ3
- ♣ AK72

Vul: Both; Dealer: South

South	West	North	East
1NT	P	2♦[1]	P
2♥	P	4♦[2]	X
4♥	P	4NT[3]	P
5♥[4]	P	6♥	All Pass

1. Transfer.
2. Singleton or void.
3. RKC.
4. 2 or 5 Key Cards without the trump Q.

Lead: ♦4. Plan the play.

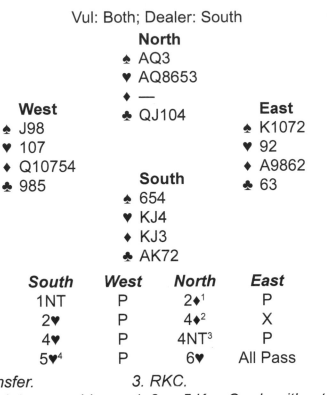

Vul: Both; Dealer: South

North
♠ AQ3
♥ AQ8653
♦ —
♣ QJ104

West
♠ J98
♥ 107
♦ Q10754
♣ 985

East
♠ K1072
♥ 92
♦ A9862
♣ 63

South
♠ 654
♥ KJ4
♦ KJ3
♣ AK72

South	West	North	East
1NT	P	2♦¹	P
2♥	P	4♦²	X
4♥	P	4NT³	P
5♥⁴	P	6♥	All Pass

1. *Transfer.*
2. *Singleton or void.*
3. *RKC.*
4. *2 or 5 Key Cards without the trump Q.*

Lead: ♦4. Plan the play.

Ruff the Diamond, draw trump and finesse the Spade. If it wins you are home. If not, you are down. If the hand was this simple would we write about it? If you can afford to lose a trick, having a Kx(xx) opposite a void presents an opportunity if LHO leads the suit. Look what happens if, instead of ruffing the Diamond lead, you discard a low Spade–a trick you were going to lose anyway. *East takes the ♦A promoting your ♦K.* Guess where the ♠Q can go!! The need for a Spade finesse just vanished. What you thought was a 50% slam is a sure thing once West leads a Diamond and you play the ♠3. West did not err. The result was just unlucky. What would you lead after partner's double asked for a Diamond lead? *When an Opponent leads a suit where you have a void consider not ruffing if you have a loser to pitch and doing so will promote a card in the other hand.* You give up one trick but get two. Is using RKC with a void right? Sometimes. This hand could make only 5♥ or make 7♥ depending on South's Key Cards and outside Kings.

Defer Drawing Trump

One of the problems facing declarer is when to draw trump. When we first learn the game we are taught to draw trump to keep the Opponents from trumping one of our tricks in an outside suit. How can an improving player know when it is right to draw trump?

Draw trump as soon as possible *unless there is something else that should be done first or something that should be done instead of drawing trump.* There are some hands where you should not draw trump, at least not immediately.

This decision should be made before playing to the first trick. Look at where your losers are. Count where your winners are and then make a plan.

We are going to present a number of hands that will help you recognize when deferring or avoiding drawing trump is best. We will start with an easy one so that you get the idea.

North	
♠ K65	
♥ 932	
♦ A9	
♣ KQ754	

Vul: None; Dealer: South

South	West	North	East
1♠	P	2♣	P
2♦	P	4♠	All Pass

Lead: ♥K. Plan the play.

South	
♠ AQJ93	
♥ A75	
♦ K83	
♣ 93	

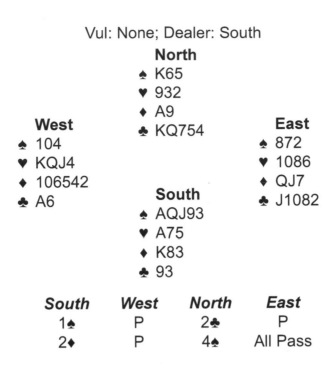

Vul: None; Dealer: South

North
♠ K65
♥ 932
♦ A9
♣ KQ754

West
♠ 104
♥ KQJ4
♦ 106542
♣ A6

East
♠ 872
♥ 1086
♦ QJ7
♣ J1082

South
♠ AQJ93
♥ A75
♦ K83
♣ 93

South	West	North	East
1♠	P	2♣	P
2♦	P	4♠	All Pass

Lead: ♥K. Plan the play.

You start with three unavoidable losers: two in Hearts and one in Clubs. You can ruff Declarer's third Diamond but not if you start by drawing all of the trumps because doing so will require at least 3 rounds. Instead, win the Ace of Hearts, lead a low Diamond to the Ace and return to the King. Then ruff Declarer's third Diamond in Dummy. Now it is safe to draw trump and drive out the Ace of Clubs. There is a slight chance that one of the Opponents has only two Diamonds and will be able to over-ruff Dummy. That does not mean that you should ruff with the ♠K. There is a greater chance of a 4–1 trump split than a 6–2 Diamond split and you will need your top 4 Spades if that happens. You could try leading up to the ♣KQ twice and pitching a Diamond on your second Club winner but that only works 50% of the time. Planning to ruff your third Diamond is far better. You can minimize the small risk of having your third Diamond over-ruffed by drawing exactly 2 rounds of trump before playing Diamonds. That way, if the Opponent short in Diamonds only has 2 trump you will be safe. You should plan to keep at least one trump in Dummy to trump your third Diamond.

Standard Card Combinations

There are certain card combinations that come up again and again. An improving player can save a lot of mental energy by learning many of these so that they can conserve that energy while getting the play right. We are going to present a number of these card combinations throughout the book so that you can learn them now and apply them at the table.

North
- ♠ KQ9
- ♥ 1086
- ♦ 9632
- ♣ AQ10

Vul: Both; Dealer: West

West	North	East	South
P	P	P	1♠
P	2♣¹	P	4♠
All Pass 2D			

South
- ♠ A10532
- ♥ 53
- ♦ AKQJ
- ♣ 84

1. Limit raise with 3+ Spades.

Lead: ♥K. East plays the ♥9 (standard signals). West plays the ♥4 to East's ♥A. East returns the ♥2 and West plays the ♥7 after you ruff low. Now what?

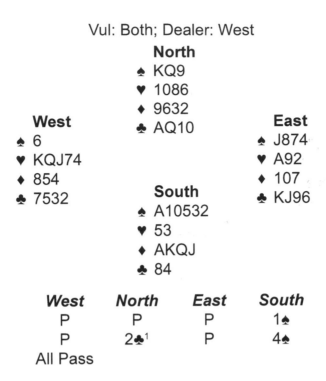

Vul: Both; Dealer: West

North
♠ KQ9
♥ 1086
♦ 9632
♣ AQ10

West
♠ 6
♥ KQJ74
♦ 854
♣ 7532

East
♠ J874
♥ A92
♦ 107
♣ KJ96

South
♠ A10532
♥ 53
♦ AKQJ
♣ 84

West	North	East	South
P	P	P	1♠
P	2♠¹	P	4♠
All Pass			

1. Limit raise with 3+ Spades.

Lead: ♥K. East plays the ♥9 (standard signals). West plays the ♥4 to East's ♥A. East returns the ♥2 and West plays the ♥7 after you ruff low. Now what?

You have lost two Hearts and the Club finesse might fail. Will Spades come home without a loser? If Spades are 3–2 there is no problem. If Spades are 5–0 in either direction or if the Jxxx is to your left you have a certain loser. Do not worry about those layouts. What about ♠Jxxx to your right? That can be solved. The 4–1 division will be exposed on the second Spade trick. A thoughtful Declarer will take the *second* Spade trick in Dummy so that, should West show out, South can take the proven Spade finesse toward the ♠A10. Since the ♠A must be preserved for the third Spade trick, the first two Spades must be taken by the ♠KQ. This is a common layout where some bad breaks can be handled and some cannot. Focus your energies on those layouts that you can overcome and forget the others. Planning at trick one is the key to meeting challenges such as this one. You can be sure that dealing with possible 4–1 splits will come up later.

Matchpoints Versus Imps

Most pairs games use matchpoint scoring. On each hand your partnership earns one matchpoint for each pair you beat, half a matchpoint for each pair you tie and zero matchpoints for each pair that beats you. It does not matter whether the difference is 10 points or 1,100. Any difference results in the award of a matchpoint. For that reason good declarers playing matchpoints will sometimes jeopardize their contract if they feel that making an overtrick is a strong possibility. After all, earning 600 for 3NT making nine tricks yields zero matchpoints if every other pair makes 10 tricks.

Team games (Knockouts or Swiss Teams) are usually scored using International Match Points (IMPs). IMPs are based on the size of the difference between each side's score. Going down in a vulnerable game that the other side makes can cost you 12 IMPs (−100 versus −620 is a net loss of 720 for 12 IMPs). Such a result, whether for or against you, often goes a long way toward deciding a match. For that reason good IMP players often give up a likely overtrick in order to guarantee making the contract. They are willing to give up one IMP in order to give themselves the best possible chance of making their contract. This is true in partials, but it is even more important in games and slams. Does it make sense to risk 10 or 12 IMPs in order to win one?

The method of scoring, matchpoints or IMPs, therefore strongly influences declarer's choice of strategy. We are going to present a series of hands that examine these choices. One set of hands for North/South will be presented multiple times; sometimes at matchpoints and sometimes at IMPs. The defensive cards will be rearranged to illustrate the differences in the strategy that should be used. Sometimes the opening lead will be changed to provide a reasonable lead from West.

Strip and End Plays

All bridge players hate hands where they have a suit with something such as A105 facing KJ7. You have a two-way finesse and guessing only works 50% of the time. What you want is for one of the Opponents to lead the suit. Forcing an Opponent to lead the suit you want them to lead is the objective of a Strip and End Play.

There are two components to the play. First you *strip* away all of the Opponent's safe exit cards. Then you put the Opponent on lead – the *end play*. The Opponent is forced to lead the suit you want led, for example, to solve a two-way finesse problem.

We are going to present a number of these problems. The first task is recognizing the possibility of making such a play. The second task is creating the end play result that you seek. This takes planning. Our explanations will help you learn how to do it. Some students find it helpful to deal out the 4 hands shown and play the tricks to see what happens from the Opponents' point of view.

North	Vul: None; Dealer: South
♠ KJ43	
♥ AJ3	
♦ 965	
♣ A73	

South	West	North	East
1♠	P	2NT[1]	P
4♠[2]	All Pass		

1. *Game force with 4 card support.*
2. *Minimum opening hand.*

South
♠ AQ652
♥ K105
♦ 84
♣ K62

Lead: ♦K. East plays an encouraging ♦7. West continues with the ♦Q and ♦J. You trump the third round. Now what?

A Declarer's Workbook

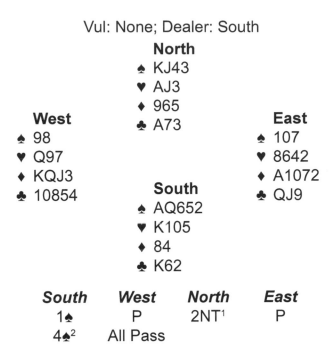

Vul: None; Dealer: South

North
- ♠ KJ43
- ♥ AJ3
- ♦ 965
- ♣ A73

West
- ♠ 98
- ♥ Q97
- ♦ KQJ3
- ♣ 10854

East
- ♠ 107
- ♥ 8642
- ♦ A1072
- ♣ QJ9

South
- ♠ AQ652
- ♥ K105
- ♦ 84
- ♣ K62

South	West	North	East
1♠	P	2NT¹	P
4♠²	All Pass		

1. *Game force with 4 card support.*
2. *Minimum opening hand.*

Lead: ♦K. East plays an encouraging ♦7. West continues with the ♦Q and ♦J. You trump the third round. Now what?

You have 3 sure losers: 2 Diamonds and a Club. Trump looks safe but what about Hearts? If you lead Hearts you have to guess where the ♥Q is. But if you can force either Opponent to lead Hearts your worries are over. When you have square (or almost square) hands and an excess of trump in both hands you have the basic ingredients for a *strip and end play*. A key element is to find an exit card so that you throw in the Opponents when they have no safe exit. After drawing trump, lead the ♣K and then small to the ♣A and ♣3. Whichever Opponent wins the third Club trick must either lead a Heart or a minor suit. If they lead a Heart you duck and win the trick as cheaply as possible. If they lead a minor suit you discard a Heart from one hand while ruffing in the other. You have executed a textbook strip and end play. The Opponents stripped Diamonds for you. You stripped Clubs by playing the ♣A and ♣K before giving up a Club trick. Whoever wins the Club trick has no safe exit.

Dummy Reversal

The term "Dummy Reversal" requires explanation. What we are "reversing" is the long trump suit for the short trump suit. In "Ruffing in the Short Hand" we said that we usually cannot create tricks by ruffing in the "long" hand. Actually, sometimes we **can** create tricks by ruffing in the long hand if we can ruff enough tricks so that the "short" hand eventually has more trump than the "long" hand.

For this strategy to work the short hand must have enough entries to make multiple ruffs possible and the short hand's trump holding must be strong enough to draw trump after those ruffs have been taken.

With a 5–3 trump fit you might be able to ruff 3 times in the long suit before drawing trump. If Dummy's 3 trump are big enough and if trump were divided 3–2 you could draw trump using the "short" suit. You will have reversed the "long" suit and the "short" suit. If the cards you hold allow you to do it, you can indeed create tricks by ruffing in the "long" hand. Here is an example.

North	
♠ K73	
♥ KQJ	
♦ 9654	
♣ A75	

Vul: None; Dealer: North

North	East	South	West
1♦	P	1♥	P
1NT	P	2♣[1]	P
2♥[2]	P	4♥	All Pass

South	
♠ A864	
♥ A9754	
♦ 8	
♣ K84	

1. Do you have 3 Hearts?
2. Yes.

Lead: ♦K. East encourages with the ♦10 and West continues with the ♦J. Plan the play.

Vul: None; Dealer: North

North
♠ K73
♥ KQJ
♦ 9654
♣ A75

West
♠ 105
♥ 863
♦ KQJ3
♣ J932

East
♠ QJ92
♥ 102
♦ A1072
♣ Q106

South
♠ A864
♥ A9754
♦ 8
♣ K84

North	East	South	West
1♦	P	1♥	P
1NT	P	2♣¹	P
2♥²	P	4♥	All Pass

1. Do you have 3 Hearts?
2. Yes.

Lead: ♦K. East encourages with the ♦10 and West continues with the ♦J. Plan the play.

If you draw trumps immediately you get no ruffs in Dummy. That leaves you with a loser each in Diamonds and Clubs and 2 losers in Spades unless the Spades split 3–3 – a 36% chance. Instead do this. Ruff the second Diamond low. Cross to the ♣A and ruff another Diamond low. Next lead the ♠4 to the ♠K and play Dummy's last Diamond but ruff with the ♥A to unblock. Now lead the ♥7 to the ♥K. The ♥Q and ♥J draw the Opponents' trump while you discard the ♥9 and the ♠4 from your hand. Lastly, lead Dummy's ♣5 to the ♣K and play the ♠A. You have ruffed 3 Diamonds in hand, drawn trump with 3 Hearts on the board. With 2 tricks each in Spades and Clubs you have 10 tricks. Since you had a singleton Diamond in hand, three top trump in Dummy and 2 high cards in Spades and Clubs you had the transportation necessary to ruff 3 Diamonds and still get to Dummy to draw trump. All you needed was a 3–2 Heart split, a 68% chance. That is not 100% but it is far better than the 36% chance of 3–3 Spades.

A Declarer's Workbook

Section Two

Exercises Using the Techniques Introduced in Section One

The exercises we have compiled have been shuffled like a deck of cards. You have no idea what kind of problem will present itself when you turn the page.

Exercise 1

Vul: Both; Dealer: East

North
- ♠ K75
- ♥ AJ74
- ♦ 85
- ♣ A752

South
- ♠ Q3
- ♥ K65
- ♦ AQ64
- ♣ KQ104

East	South	West	North
P	1NT	P	2♣
P	2♦	P	3NT
All Pass			

Lead: ♠10. You duck on the board and win the ♠Q. Where are your nine tricks going to come from?

Combining Your Chances

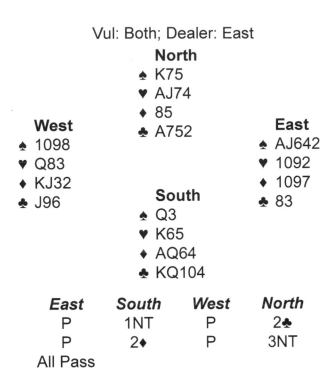

Vul: Both; Dealer: East

North
♠ K75
♥ AJ74
♦ 85
♣ A752

West
♠ 1098
♥ Q83
♦ KJ32
♣ J96

East
♠ AJ642
♥ 1092
♦ 1097
♣ 83

South
♠ Q3
♥ K65
♦ AQ64
♣ KQ104

East	South	West	North
P	1NT	P	2♣
P	2♦	P	3NT
All Pass			

Lead: ♠10. You duck on the board and win the ♠Q. Where are your nine tricks going to come from?

Assuming you take four Club tricks you have eight tricks. The ninth trick could come from a finesse in either Hearts or Diamonds. One of two finesses will work approximately 75% of the time while a single finesse works only 50% of the time. That is a great combining tool but be careful. Often the order in which you take the finesses matters. Notice that your ♠K is exposed. West is the dangerous hand because a Spade lead will trap your ♠K. If you try the Diamond finesse first your contract could fail without your ever trying the Heart finesse. Take your first finesse in Hearts. If it loses East cannot attack your ♠K. You can win any return and try the Diamond finesse later. Before taking the Diamond finesse check if the Hearts are 3–3. Usually they will not be but it costs nothing to try. Play the ♥A and then the ♥K. If Hearts were 3–3 you have 9 tricks. If not, take the Diamond finesse, your last chance. One last thing is important. When you play Clubs remember this card combination. By playing the ♣K and then the ♣A you will be able to survive a 4–1 break to your right. Prepare for it!

Exercise 2

Vul: E/W; Dealer: East

North
- ♠ 9843
- ♥ K7
- ♦ Q86
- ♣ AJ104

K - Cl
10 - 9/0

South
- ♠ A765
- ♥ A842
- ♦ AK3
- ♣ 95

East	South	West	North
P	1NT	P	2♣
P	2♥	P	3NT
P	4♠	All Pass	

Lead: ♦5. Plan the play.

Weak Trump Suit
Ruffing

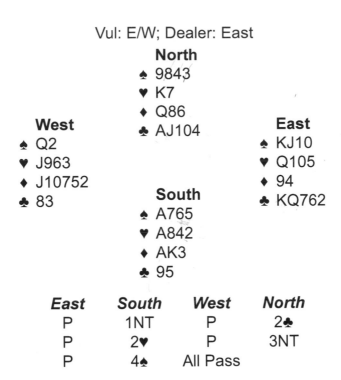

Vul: E/W; Dealer: East

North
♠ 9843
♥ K7
♦ Q86
♣ AJ104

West
♠ Q2
♥ J963
♦ J10752
♣ 83

East
♠ KJ10
♥ Q105
♦ 94
♣ KQ762

South
♠ A765
♥ A842
♦ AK3
♣ 95

East	South	West	North
P	1NT	P	2♣
P	2♥	P	3NT
P	4♠	All Pass	

Lead: ♦5. Plan the play.

A nice auction has you in a playable contract but the weak trump suit is a threat. You must make maximum use of your small trumps to come to 10 tricks. If trump break badly then you have 3 trump losers plus a Club loser so assume trump are 3–2. Your goal should be to ruff 2 Hearts in Dummy. You start with 2 losers in trump and 1 in Clubs. If 3 rounds of trump are played you will be left with a losing Heart and no place to put it. Start by drawing 2 rounds of trump but be careful how you do it! Duck one round and win the second and leave the last trump out. If you play the ♠A first the defender winning the second trump could play a third round and prevent your ruffing 2 Hearts. Win the opening lead with the ♦Q and duck a round of trumps. Win any return and play the ♠A but leave the last high trump outstanding. Now play the ♥K and ♥A and ruff a heart. Get back to your hand with a Diamond and ruff your last Heart. The Opponent with the remaining trump cannot gain by overruffing either Heart ruff or the Diamond lead back to your hand. You lose 2 trump and a Club but make your contract.

A Declarer's Workbook

Exercise 3

Vul: E/W; Dealer: North

North
♠ A1085
♥ K104
♦ AJ42
♣ 97

2 Clubs

South
♠ KJ763
♥ Q62
♦ KQ7
♣ K8

North	East	South	West
1♦	P	1♠	2♣
2♠	P	4♠	All Pass

Lead: ♦10. Plan the play.

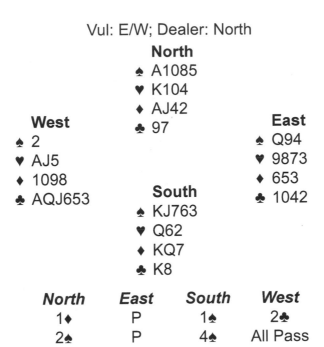

Vul: E/W; Dealer: North

North
♠ A1085
♥ K104
♦ AJ42
♣ 97

West
♠ 2
♥ AJ5
♦ 1098
♣ AQJ653

East
♠ Q94
♥ 9873
♦ 653
♣ 1042

South
♠ KJ763
♥ Q62
♦ KQ7
♣ K8

North	East	South	West
1♦	P	1♠	2♣
2♠	P	4♠	All Pass

Lead: ♦10. Plan the play.

You start with 5 possible losers. One can go on the fourth Diamond but you must to draw trump first. With 9 trumps do you try to drop the ♠Q? That is what "Eight Ever Nine Never" says but that dictum usually should not be applied when one hand on lead (East in this hand) is more dangerous than the other. Moreover, the bidding allows you to draw a pretty clear picture of West's hand. The ♥A and the ♣AQJ are needed for the 2♣ bid and West does not need the ♠Q. Shortness in Spades would suffice and is more likely. East probably holds the ♠Qxx(x). All the evidence points that way. Win trick one with the ♦K and lead low to the ♠A. If West shows out you have a marked finesse. If not, lead the ♠10 and finesse it unless East covers. Even if this finesse loses West cannot attack your ♣K. You can hold your Heart losers to one by playing West for the ♥AJx(x), a likely holding on the bidding. Finish drawing trump and run your Diamonds, pitching a Club. Give up a Club in order to get to hand with a Club ruff so that you can lead up to the ♥10. If West holds the ♥J you will make your contract even if the Spade finesse loses. You will lose only three tricks – a Club, a Heart and a Spade. On this bidding the chances of locating the ♠Q with East is high. You have two chances: finding either the ♠Q or the ♥J.

Exercise 4

Vul: Both; Dealer: East

North
- ♠ J842
- ♥ A7532
- ♦ Q65
- ♣ 7

South
- ♠ 93
- ♥ K6
- ♦ AK973
- ♣ A1084

East	South	West	North
P	1♦	P	1♥
P	2♣	P	2♦
All Pass			

Lead: ♦8. Plan the play.

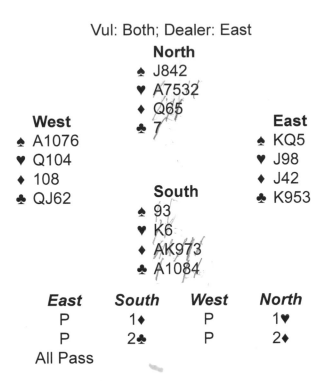

Vul: Both; Dealer: East

North
♠ J842
♥ A7532
♦ Q65
♣ 7

West
♠ A1076
♥ Q104
♦ 108
♣ QJ62

East
♠ KQ5
♥ J98
♦ J42
♣ K953

South
♠ 93
♥ K6
♦ AK973
♣ A1084

East	South	West	North
P	1♦	P	1♥
P	2♣	P	2♦
All Pass			

Lead: ♦8. Plan the play.

If Diamonds are 3–2 you have 8 tricks. If you draw trump and take your 8 tricks you will likely lose 2 IMPs in a team game or get a bottom board at Matchpoints. What is worse, if Diamonds split badly your contract will fail. West's trump lead is good defense but you can prevail. If you draw trump immediately your ♦6 and ♦5 win nothing. Instead, win the ♦Q and lead the ♣7 to the ♣A. Ruff a Club and get back to your hand with the ♥K. Now ruff another Club. How do you get back to your hand? Do not touch Hearts! You can take your ♥A after you draw trump. Instead, lead a small Spade. Eventually you will get back to your hand by ruffing a Spade with a low trump. Now you play your ♦A and ♦K. If Diamonds were 3–2 you will make 10 tricks, not 8. If Diamonds are 4–1 or 5–0 your Club ruffs with the ♦6 and ♦5 guarantee your contract. This deal is a great example of the importance of ruffing in the short hand.

A Declarer's Workbook

Exercise 5

Don't Understand?

Vul: N/S; Dealer: South
Scoring: Matchpoints

North
♠ K7
♥ A65
♦ K754
♣ K642

South
♠ A43
♥ KQ1032
♦ A82
♣ Q3

South	*West*	*North*	*East*
1♥	P	2♣[1]	P
2NT	P	4♥	All Pass

1. Game Forcing.

Lead: ♦Q. Plan the play.

Lose 1D
1C
Maybe 1H

Vul: N/S; Dealer: South; Scoring: Matchpoints

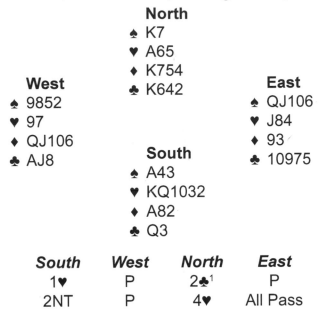

North
♠ K7
♥ A65
♦ K754
♣ K642

West
♠ 9852
♥ 97
♦ QJ106
♣ AJ8

East
♠ QJ106
♥ J84
♦ 93
♣ 10975

South
♠ A43
♥ KQ1032
♦ A82
♣ Q3

South	West	North	East
1♥	P	2♣¹	P
2NT	P	4♥	All Pass

1. Game Forcing.

Lead: ♦Q. Plan the play.

You have one loser each in Diamonds and Clubs. Because this is Matchpoints you should consider trying to ruff a Spade in Dummy before completely drawing trump to make 11 tricks. Beware!! There is a trap you can avoid. Before playing Spades test the distribution of trump by playing the ♥K and ♥A in that order. If trump are 3–2 play the ♠K and ♠A and ruff a Spade to avoid a Spade loser. If trump are 4–1 with East abandon the Spade ruff to finesse trump through East to avoid a trump loser. If trump are 4–1 with West you have a sure trump loser and ruffing a Spade before drawing three rounds of trump becomes mandatory. West would not gain by ruffing your third Spade because you would then be able to draw West's last trump. It is right to want to ruff a Spade in Dummy but doing so risks the contract unnecessarily if trump are 4–1 with East. This risk can be avoided by playing the ♥K and ♥A before playing Spades.

Exercise 6

Vul: Both; Dealer: West

North
- ♠ 873
- ♥ A1096
- ♦ K107
- ♣ KQ5

South
- ♠ 105
- ♥ KJ532
- ♦ AJ5
- ♣ A86

West	North	East	South
P	1♣	P	1♥
P	2♥	P	4♥
All Pass			

Lead: ♠K. East encourages with the ♠6 and West continues with the ♠Q & ♠J. You ruff. Since "nine never" seems to apply you play the ♥A and ♥K but the lady fails to appear, giving you a certain third loser plus a possible fourth loser in the ♦Q. What now?

Vul: Both; Dealer: West

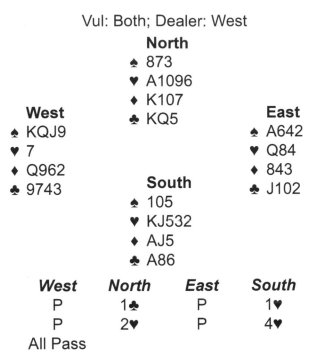

North
- ♠ 873
- ♥ A1096
- ♦ K107
- ♣ KQ5

West
- ♠ KQJ9
- ♥ 7
- ♦ Q962
- ♣ 9743

East
- ♠ A642
- ♥ Q84
- ♦ 843
- ♣ J102

South
- ♠ 105
- ♥ KJ532
- ♦ AJ5
- ♣ A86

West	North	East	South
P	1♣	P	1♥
P	2♥	P	4♥
All Pass			

Lead: ♠K. East encourages with the ♠6 and West continues with the ♠Q & ♠J. You ruff. Since "nine never" seems to apply you play the ♥A and ♥K but the lady fails to appear, giving you a certain third loser plus a possible fourth loser in the ♦Q. What now?

Do not try to guess the location of the ♦Q. And whatever you do, do not draw East's ♥Q. That is the key card; the all-important throw in card!! You can make East find the ♦Q for you or give you a ruff and discard. You do this by running your Clubs. If East trumps any Club the result will be an end play because East will have only Spades and Diamonds. If East does not trump a Club then lead a Heart, forcing East to win the ♥Q. East is trapped. If a black card is lead you will discard a Diamond from one hand and trump in the other, thereby eliminating your potential Diamond loser. If East chooses to lead a Diamond you play your ♦5. Regardless of who has the ♦Q your Diamond loser has vanished. This is a particularly enjoyable play if East was smirking when the ♥Q did not fall. There are two key plays: (1) stripping Clubs from your hand and Dummy's and (2) leaving the ♥Q outstanding and then using it to throw East in the lead when no safe exit is possible.

A Declarer's Workbook

Exercise 7

Vul: None; Dealer: South

North
- ♠ AK84
- ♥ 93
- ♦ 864
- ♣ KJ92

South
- ♠ 952
- ♥ A75
- ♦ AKJ10
- ♣ A105

South	West	North	East
1NT	P	2♣	P
2♦	P	3NT	All Pass

Lead: ♥Q. East plays the ♥4 (standard signals). Plan the play.

Let it go twice

A C

10 C

Vul: None; Dealer: South

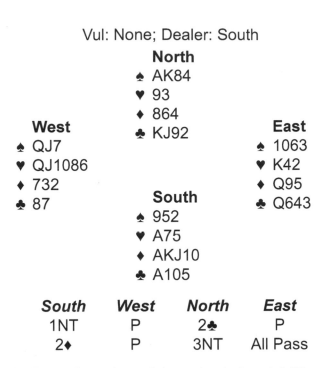

North
- ♠ AK84
- ♥ 93
- ♦ 864
- ♣ KJ92

West
- ♠ QJ7
- ♥ QJ1086
- ♦ 732
- ♣ 87

East
- ♠ 1063
- ♥ K42
- ♦ Q95
- ♣ Q643

South
- ♠ 952
- ♥ A75
- ♦ AKJ10
- ♣ A105

South	West	North	East
1NT	P	2♣	P
2♦	P	3NT	All Pass

Lead: ♥Q. East plays the ♥4 (standard signals) Plan the play.

Do you duck the ♥A? If Hearts are 4–4 it does not matter. They can only win 3 Hearts and you will have time to try both minor suit finesses. But if Hearts are 5–3 or worse ducking is necessary. If you duck twice you can run East out of Hearts. East will not be able to lead a Heart to West after winning a subsequent trick. There is no way to know the Heart distribution at trick one so you better duck. West continues Hearts with East overtaking the ♥K and you duck again. When East leads the ♥2 (East's last Heart) you win and try Clubs, not Diamonds, by finessing the ♣10 into East, preserving the ♣A as an entry. If this wins you are home. If it loses East cannot lead a Heart. Win any return and play the A, K and J of Diamonds in that order. This approach is better than a finesse because it wins if East has the ♦Q or West has the ♦Q singleton or doubleton. You go down only if West has 3 or more Diamonds to the Queen. There are several important points. You must duck Hearts until trick 3 to exhaust Hearts in East's hand to break communication. Then you have to take the Club finesse into East before trying the Diamond finesse. If the Diamond finesse loses you have a disaster on your hands. Save that finesse until you have nothing else left.

A Declarer's Workbook

Exercise 8

Vul: Both; Dealer: West

North
- ♠ K1042
- ♥ 85
- ♦ AJ2
- ♣ A1094

South
- ♠ AJ83
- ♥ A43
- ♦ Q64
- ♣ K32

West	North	East	South
P	1♣	P	1♠
P	2♠	P	4♠
All Pass			

Lead: ♥K. Plan the play.

Lose 1st H
Take 2nd H
Trump 3rd H

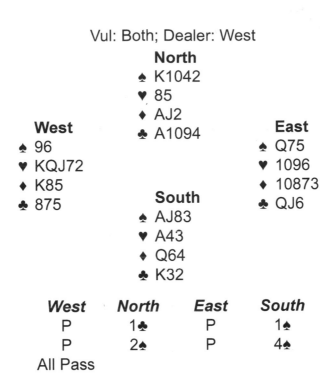

Vul: Both; Dealer: West

North
♠ K1042
♥ 85
♦ AJ2
♣ A1094

West
♠ 96
♥ KQJ72
♦ K85
♣ 875

East
♠ Q75
♥ 1096
♦ 10873
♣ QJ6

South
♠ AJ83
♥ A43
♦ Q64
♣ K32

West	North	East	South
P	1♣	P	1♠
P	2♠	P	4♠
All Pass			

Lead: ♥K. Plan the play.

You have four possible losers: one per suit. First find the ♠Q. Is "Eight Ever, Nine Never" right? East and West were silent during the auction. Neither Opponent is more dangerous than the other. There is no advantage to playing one Opponent for the Queen over the other. "Eight Ever, Nine Ever" applies. Declarer, holding eight Spades, should take the finesse but which way is right? It is a guess, but use good technique when making the play. First attempt to drop a singleton Queen. <u>Duck the first Heart and win the second</u>. This insures that you get your Heart ruff if trump break badly. Win the ♥A, ruff your last Heart and play Dummy's ♠K. If the Queen falls congratulate yourself for making a play that allowed you to be lucky. If the Queen does not fall lead the ♠10 to pick up a 4–1 Spade split. On the layout shown you come up a winner. The finesse will lose half the time but that is far better than the 1/3 chance of dropping the ♠Q by playing the Ace and King. Once trump are drawn work on Clubs before Diamonds. If Clubs are 3–3 or 4–2 with either the ♣Q or ♣J doubleton you can establish Dummy's fourth club as a resting spot for South's ♦4. Play the ♣K, ♣A and ♣10 in that order.

Exercise 9

Vul: None; Dealer: North

North
- ♠ KJ93
- ♥ 8643
- ♦ A97
- ♣ A7

South
- ♠ AQ1042
- ♥ —
- ♦ K542
- ♣ 8632

North	East	South	West
1♦	P	1♠	2♥
2♠	3♥	4♠	All Pass

Lead: ♥A (Ace from AK). East follows with the ♥2. Plan the play.

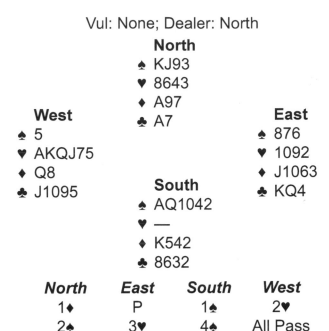

Vul: None; Dealer: North

North
♠ KJ93
♥ 8643
♦ A97
♣ A7

West
♠ 5
♥ AKQJ75
♦ Q8
♣ J1095

East
♠ 876
♥ 1092
♦ J1063
♣ KQ4

South
♠ AQ1042
♥ —
♦ K542
♣ 8632

North	East	South	West
1♦	P	1♠	2♥
2♠	3♥	4♠	All Pass

Lead: ♥A (Ace from AK). East follows with the ♥2. Plan the play.

Unless Diamonds are 3–3 you have two Diamond losers and three Club losers. You can ruff a Diamond and a Club in Dummy, but must lose a trick in each suit first. Additionally, trump are more likely to be 3–1 or 4–0 than 2–2. If you draw a round of trump before giving up those minor suit tricks and trump are not 2–2 the defender winning each minor suit trick could lead a trump. That would reduce Dummy's trump holding to one, thereby preventing you from getting two minor suit ruffs in Dummy. ***You must defer leading trump until you have lost the two minor suit tricks.*** The defenders can lead trump each time they are in but they cannot reduce Dummy's trump holding to less than two unless you help them by leading trump yourself. The chances of the ♣A being ruffed are almost zero but there is a chance of Diamonds being 5–1. The bidding tells you that West has Heart length so Diamond shortness is more likely with West. Ruff the ♥A, lead to the ♣A and concede a Club. If the Opponent leads a Diamond win the ♦K. If anything else is led win that trick and lead to the ♦K. Next lead up to the ♦A. If West ruffs you must duck, thereby losing the necessary Diamond trick. You can win any return and enjoy a high crossruff. Sometimes waiting to draw trump is necessary.

A Declarer's Workbook

Exercise 10

Vul: N/S; Dealer: South

North
- ♠ AQ7
- ♥ KQ6
- ♦ J4
- ♣ K10964

South
- ♠ K654
- ♥ A53
- ♦ 87
- ♣ AQ73

South	West	North	East
1♣	P	2♣[1]	P
2♥[2]	P	2♠[3]	P
3♣	P	5♣	All Pass

1. *Limit raise or better in Clubs denying a 4 card Major.*
2. *Heart stopper denying a Diamond stopper.*
3. *Spade stopper.*

Lead: ♦A. East follows with the ♦10 to show the ♦Q. West wins the ♦K and shifts to the ♠10. What is your plan?

Vul: N/S; Dealer: South

North
- ♠ AQ7
- ♥ KQ6
- ♦ J4
- ♣ K10964

West
- ♠ 1098
- ♥ 107
- ♦ AK32
- ♣ J852

East
- ♠ J32
- ♥ J9842
- ♦ Q10965
- ♣ —

South
- ♠ K654
- ♥ A53
- ♦ 87
- ♣ AQ73

South	West	North	East
1♣	P	2♣¹	P
2♥²	P	2♠³	P
3♣	P	5♣	All Pass

1. *Limit raise or better in Clubs denying a 4 card Major.*
2. *Heart stopper denying a Diamond stopper.*
3. *Spade stopper.*

Lead: ♦A. East follows with the ♦10 to show the ♦Q. West wins the ♦K and shifts to the ♠10. What is your plan?

After finding the lack of a Diamond stopper you get to a good 5♣ contract. After losing the first two Diamond tricks it looks like the next 11 tricks are yours. At times such as this, expert players ask themselves what could possibly go wrong. If you fail to do this you might carelessly lead a low Club to the King, thereby creating a trump loser. Your thinking should go like this: The only thing that can defeat me is a 4–0 Club break. I can finesse for the ♣J in either direction. If I start with the ♣A I will know if there is a 4–0 break and which way to take the Club finesse. This is an easy problem to solve once you ask yourself the right question: "What can possibly go wrong?" When all looks rosy become a pessimist. Ask yourself what could go wrong and then design your play to detect the problem and solve it.

A Declarer's Workbook

Exercise 11

Vul: None; Dealer: East

North
- ♠ AJ653
- ♥ K3
- ♦ 8752
- ♣ 97

South
- ♠ KQ92
- ♥ AJ65
- ♦ 643
- ♣ AQ

East	South	West	North
P	1NT	P	2♥
P	2♠	P	2NT
P	4♠	All Pass	

Lead: ♦J to East's A, K, Q and 9 with West discarding on the third Diamond. Plan the play.

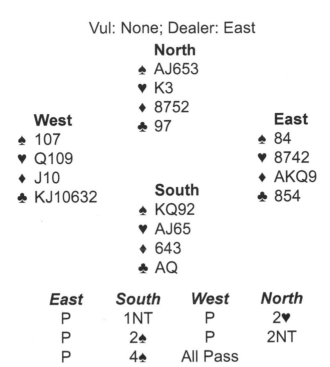

Vul: None; Dealer: East

North
♠ AJ653
♥ K3
♦ 8752
♣ 97

West
♠ 107
♥ Q109
♦ J10
♣ KJ10632

East
♠ 84
♥ 8742
♦ AKQ9
♣ 854

South
♠ KQ92
♥ AJ65
♦ 643
♣ AQ

East	South	West	North
P	1NT	P	2♥
P	2♠	P	2NT
P	4♠	All Pass	

Lead: ♦J to East's A, K, Q and 9 with West discarding on the third Diamond. Plan the play.

West is out of Diamonds. Do you ruff with the ♠K or ♠9? There is more space in West's hand than East's for the ♠10 so West will have it most of the time. A 4–0 split in Spades, while possible, is far less likely. Play the ♠K at trick four to protect against the more likely problem. Turning to the rest of the play, is the Club finesse your only chance? The Heart finesse could allow you to pitch one of Dummy's Clubs but that would just trade one 50% chance for another. You have 6 Hearts so the Opponents have 7. The ♥Q could fall in three rounds. If the Queen appears you have a parking place for a small Club in Dummy, thereby avoiding the Club finesse. If the ♥Q does not fall you still have the lead so you can try the Club finesse. Your contract fails only if the ♥Q does not drop and the Club finesse loses. Even though it is less than 50/50 that the ♥Q will drop it costs nothing to find out. The ♥Q falling is lucky, but only good declarers will give themselves that extra chance.

Exercise 12

Vul: Both; Dealer: West

North
♠ KQJ3
♥ A42
♦ 9742
♣ 76

South
♠ 864
♥ Q73
♦ AKQ8
♣ KQ5

West	North	East	South
P	P	P	1NT
P	2♣	P	2♦
P	3NT	All Pass	

Lead: ♥J. Plan the play.

Vul: Both; Dealer: West

North
♠ KQJ3
♥ A42
♦ 9742
♣ 76

West
♠ A9
♥ KJ1095
♦ 65
♣ J842

East
♠ 10752
♥ 86
♦ J103
♣ A1093

South
♠ 864
♥ Q73
♦ AKQ8
♣ KQ5

West	North	East	South
P	P	P	1NT
P	2♣	P	2♦
P	3NT	All Pass	

Lead: ♥J. Plan the play.

The ♥J lead gives you 2 stoppers by ducking to the ♥Q, If Diamonds behave you have 6 tricks. Where are 3 more? If Hearts are 4–3 the Opponents can win 2 Hearts in addition to the ♣A and ♠A. If Hearts are 5–2 you could lose 3 Hearts plus the black Aces. After winning the ♥Q you have 1 Heart stopper. Spades can yield 3 winners if they are 3–3 or the ♠A is with West. If Spades fail you will need a Club trick. If it comes to that and Hearts are 5–2 you are safe if East has the ♣A because East will have no more Hearts. Since there is no way to know where either black Ace lives win the ♥Q, retain your Diamonds for transportation and lead a low Spade, continuing to lead up to the ♠KQJ until the ♠A is played and the ♥A is driven out. Win any return and play out your Diamonds and Spades, ending in Dummy. If the ♠A was with West or if Spades were 3–3 you have 9 tricks and the Clubs might yield an overtrick. If Spades did not yield 3 tricks you must hope that the ♣A is with East if Hearts are 5–2. Lead up to the ♣K and hope. To summarize, because you can afford to lose the lead once you should try Spades before Clubs because if West has the ♠A or Spades are 3–3 you are safe even if Hearts are 5–2 and West has the ♣A.

A Declarer's Workbook

Exercise 13

Vul: N/S; Dealer: West

North
- ♠ A53
- ♥ Q854
- ♦ A743
- ♣ K4

South
- ♠ Q84
- ♥ A973
- ♦ K8
- ♣ A952

West	North	East	South
P	1♦	P	1♥
P	2♥	P	4♥
All Pass			

Lead: ♠J. Plan the play.

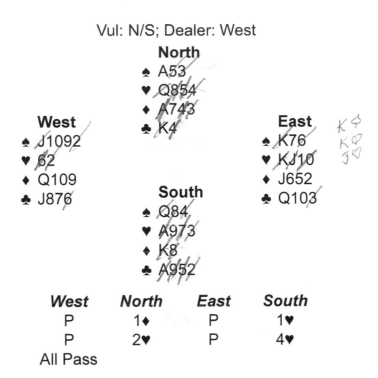

Vul: N/S; Dealer: West

North
♠ A53
♥ Q854
♦ A743
♣ K4

West
♠ J1092
♥ 62
♦ Q109
♣ J876

East
♠ K76
♥ KJ10
♦ J652
♣ Q103

South
♠ Q84
♥ A973
♦ K8
♣ A952

West	North	East	South
P	1♦	P	1♥
P	2♥	P	4♥
All Pass			

Lead: ♠J. Plan the play.

Ducking to your ♠Q holds the Spade losers to 1. There are 2 potential trump losers. Success requires an eventual cross ruff in the minors. Leaving a high trump outstanding will keep 2 trump in each hand. East will probably return a Spade after winning the ♠K. Win that and draw exactly 2 rounds of trump. The "book" play for Qxxx facing Axxx is to play the Ace in case the King is singleton and then lead up to the Queen. That is correct in isolation but that will likely fail on this hand. The primary consideration here is winning the second trump trick, thereby preventing a third trump lead. Win the second trick in hand (unless East returns a trump) and lead up to the ♥Q. If West has the ♥K you will hold your trump losers to 1. If East has the ♥K you will lose two trump but that is acceptable as long as you get your cross ruff set up. After the ♥K is lost win any return, play the ♥A and play your minor suits, eventually cross ruffing for the last four tricks. The holder of the high trump will overruff at some point but no matter. You will be able to resume your cross-ruff and score 10 or 11 tricks.

A Declarer's Workbook

Exercise 14

Vul: None; Dealer: South

North
♠ A1064
♥ K97
♦ Q53
♣ 752

South
♠ KJ7
♥ 632
♦ AKJ9
♣ AJ10

South	West	North	East
1NT	P	2♣	P
2♦	P	2NT	P
3NT	All Pass		

Lead: ♣6. East plays the ♣8 (standard signals). Plan the play.

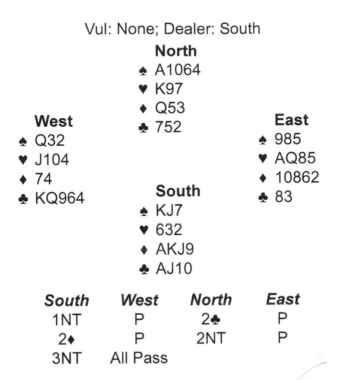

Vul: None; Dealer: South

North
- ♠ A1064
- ♥ K97
- ♦ Q53
- ♣ 752

West
- ♠ Q32
- ♥ J104
- ♦ 74
- ♣ KQ964

East
- ♠ 985
- ♥ AQ85
- ♦ 10862
- ♣ 83

South
- ♠ KJ7
- ♥ 632
- ♦ AKJ9
- ♣ AJ10

South	West	North	East
1NT	P	2♣	P
2♦	P	2NT	P
3NT	All Pass		

Lead: ♣6. East plays the ♣8 (standard signals). Plan the play.

With the opening lead you have eight tricks off the top and another coming in Spades whether the finesse wins or loses. This looks like an easy hand but be careful. Ask yourself what could go wrong. You can take the Spade finesse either way. If you take it into West's hand what bad thing could happen? West could win the ♠Q and then lead Hearts through your King. If the Hearts are sitting badly you could go down on a cold contract. Instead, take the finesse into East's hand. East cannot attack Hearts without establishing the Dummy's King. This is a simple play once you know where to look. Whenever you have a Kx(xx) or Qxx(x) opposite nothing you should be thinking about keeping the defense from leading through that weakness, particularly at No Trump.

Exercise 15

Vul: Both; Dealer: North

North
- ♠ 9875
- ♥ KQ107
- ♦ A6
- ♣ K65

A Spades

A J U

South
- ♠ 6
- ♥ AJ842
- ♦ K753
- ♣ Q43

North	East	South	West
1♣	P	1♥	1♠
2♥	2♠	4♥	All Pass

Lead: ♠A (Ace from AK) followed by the ♠Q. Plan the play.

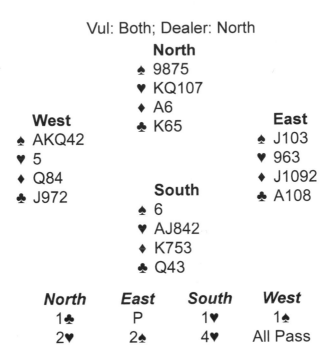

Vul: Both; Dealer: North

North
- ♠ 9875
- ♥ KQ107
- ♦ A6
- ♣ K65

West
- ♠ AKQ42
- ♥ 5
- ♦ Q84
- ♣ J972

East
- ♠ J103
- ♥ 963
- ♦ J1092
- ♣ A108

South
- ♠ 6
- ♥ AJ842
- ♦ K753
- ♣ Q43

North	East	South	West
1♣	P	1♥	1♠
2♥	2♠	4♥	All Pass

Lead: ♠A (Ace from AK) followed by the ♠Q. Plan the play.

If you ruff the ♠Q and draw trump you will score 5 trump in hand, 2 Diamond ruffs in Dummy plus 2 high Diamonds and a Club as long as trump are 2–2. If trump are 3–1 (the most likely distribution) you win only 1 Diamond ruff. You need an approach that works whether trump are 2–2 or 3–1. You need 3 Dummy entries to ruff 3 Spades and then draw trump using Dummy's high Hearts. You have sure Dummy entries as long as you ruff with the ♥A. Ruff the ♠Q with the ♥2 and lead the ♥4 to the ♥10. If both Opponents follow you can afford to later overtake your ♥J to get to Dummy. Ruff a Spade with the ♥8 and then lead the ♥J to the ♥Q. Ruff a third Spade with the ♥A followed by the ♦3 to the ♦A. Play the ♥K to draw the last trump. Concede a trick to the ♣A and claim. By winning 3 Spade ruffs in hand and 4 trump in Dummy you win 10 tricks even when trump are 3–1. Dummy Reversals can help you escape bad trump breaks. The challenge is managing entries. Did you notice that we played the ♥4 before the ♦3? That play tests the trump distribution to see if the ♥J is needed to draw trump. We will address dealing with a 4–0 trump break in another problem.

Exercise 16

Vul: N/S; Dealer: East

North
- ♠ 9532
- ♥ AJ63
- ♦ AQ3
- ♣ 75

South
- ♠ AKQ6
- ♥ K74
- ♦ 865
- ♣ A32

East	South	West	North
P	1NT	P	2♣
P	2♠	P	4♠
All Pass			

Lead: ♣K. Plan the play.

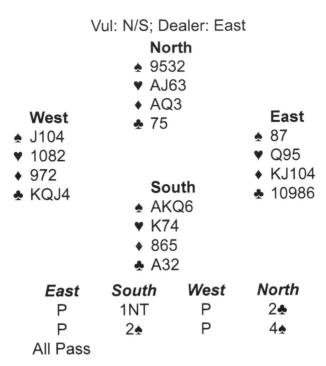

Vul: N/S; Dealer: East

North
- ♠ 9532
- ♥ AJ63
- ♦ AQ3
- ♣ 75

West
- ♠ J104
- ♥ 1082
- ♦ 972
- ♣ KQJ4

East
- ♠ 87
- ♥ Q95
- ♦ KJ104
- ♣ 10986

South
- ♠ AKQ6
- ♥ K74
- ♦ 865
- ♣ A32

East	South	West	North
P	1NT	P	2♣
P	2♠	P	4♠
All Pass			

Lead: ♣K. Plan the play.

You have a Club and possible Heart loser plus one or two Diamond losers. Lesser players will think this hand depends on one of two finesses in Hearts and Diamonds. One of two finesses is about 75% and they will be satisfied but you can do better. Whether or not the Heart finesse wins, the Hearts could split 3–3. If they do and if you can prevent an early attack on Diamonds you can pitch a Diamond on Dummy's fourth Heart. Preventing that early Diamond attack is vital so trick one merits thought. If you win it East will be able to lead to West's ♣Q if the finesse of the ♥J loses to East. West will surely lead a Diamond then because everything will be known. If you duck trick one West could shift to a Diamond immediately but West does not yet know where your values are. Without the ♦K, West might suspect that you have it because you opened 1 NT. West will likely continue Clubs. If that happens, take your Ace, draw trump and finesse the ♥J. Even if it loses East cannot attack Diamonds and can no longer get to West in Clubs because Dummy is void. Whether the Heart finesse wins or loses play two more Hearts. If they are 3–3 you pitch a Diamond. If not, ruff the last Heart and take the Diamond finesse. If West switches to a Diamond at trick 2 rise with the ♦A, draw trump and take the Heart finesse. It is your only chance.

A Declarer's Workbook

Exercise 17

Vul: Both; Dealer: East

North
- ♠ 98
- ♥ AQ104
- ♦ A105
- ♣ KJ65

South
- ♠ A75
- ♥ 962
- ♦ KJ2
- ♣ AQ84

East	South	West	North
P	1♣	1♠	X
2♠	P	P	3♠¹
P	3NT	All Pass	

1. Bid 3NT with Spades stopped. Choose a suit if not.

Lead: ♠K, ♠Q and ♠J. You hold off until the third round to run East out of Spades, pitching the ♣5. Good Play! Now what?

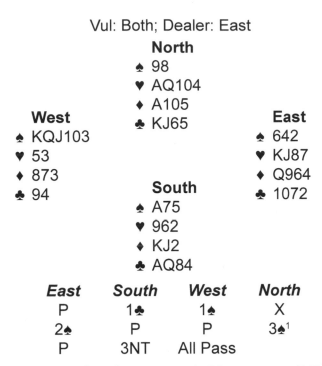

Vul: Both; Dealer: East

North
- ♠ 98
- ♥ AQ104
- ♦ A105
- ♣ KJ65

West
- ♠ KQJ103
- ♥ 53
- ♦ 873
- ♣ 94

East
- ♠ 642
- ♥ KJ87
- ♦ Q964
- ♣ 1072

South
- ♠ A75
- ♥ 962
- ♦ KJ2
- ♣ AQ84

East	South	West	North
P	1♣	1♠	X
2♠	P	P	3♠¹
P	3NT	All Pass	

1. Bid 3NT with Spades stopped. Choose a suit if not.

Lead: ♠K, ♠Q and ♠J. You hold off until the third round to run East out of Spades, pitching the ♣5. Good Play! Now what?

You have 8 tricks off the top. Finesses abound with lots of entries. Which finesse is right? You have a 100% play. Look carefully at the spot cards. The key card is your ♥9. If you take two Heart finesses into West you cannot be prevented from establishing a second Heart trick – your ninth trick. Because East has no more Spades there is no way for East to put West on lead. A Diamond lead would give you a free finesse and an overtrick while a Club lead is no threat. After winning the ♠A lead the ♥2 to the ♥10. Do not lead the ♥9 in case the ♥J is singleton. If the ♥10 wins or if it loses to the ♥K your contract is assured. If the ♥10 loses to the ♥J return to hand with a Club to run the ♥9. If that finesse wins you are safe. If it loses to the ♥K Dummy's ♥Q is now good and East still has no entry to West's hand. The lesson here is that when considering finesses consider the spot cards carefully. Sometimes, as here, the spot cards in a suit give you an additional trick regardless of where the defensive cards lie. Turn thc ♥9 into the ♥3 and you have a much more challenging problem. We will leave that for another page. Consider yourself warned!!

A Declarer's Workbook

Exercise 18

Vul: N/S; Dealer: South

North
- ♠ 109864
- ♥ A3
- ♦ K64
- ♣ K74

South
- ♠ A75
- ♥ K874
- ♦ A853
- ♣ A8

South	West	North	East
1NT	P	2♥[1]	P
2♠	P	3NT	P
4♠	All Pass		

1. Transfer to Spades.

Lead: ♣Q. East plays the ♣3 using standard signals. Plan the play.

Vul: N/S; Dealer: South

North
- ♠ 109864
- ♥ A3
- ♦ K64
- ♣ K74

West
- ♠ Q
- ♥ 952
- ♦ Q72
- ♣ QJ1092

East
- ♠ KJ32
- ♥ QJ106
- ♦ J109
- ♣ 653

South
- ♠ A75
- ♥ K874
- ♦ A853
- ♣ A8

South	West	North	East
1NT	P	2♥¹	P
2♠	P	3NT	P
4♠	All Pass		

1. Transfer to Spades.

Lead: ♣Q. East plays the ♣3 using standard signals. Plan the play.

We have learned to lead a low trump followed by the Ace to preserve trump in both hands of a weak trump suit. That approach leaves one high trump outstanding if trumps are 3–2 but it succeeds only with a 3–2 split. When we need two or more ruffs in each hand we often have to take that risk. Should we use that technique here? Only one ruff is needed in Declarer's hand – Dummy's third Club. West's ♣Q is likely the top of a sequence but West did not make a Club interference bid and East's ♣3 signals shortness only if it is a singleton or the top of a doubleton 3 and 2. The chance of either of those things is certainly less than the chance of a 4–1 trump split. A better play is to win the ♣A, ♠A and ♣K in that order and then ruff Dummy's ♣4. Declarer should then play a low Spade. This holds trump losers to 2 whenever trumps are 3–2 *or* when trumps are 4–1 and one of the three missing honors is singleton, which will happen more often than not when trumps are 4–1. Taking the Club ruff early keeps the defender winning the second trump trick from preventing the ruff of Dummy's ♣4.

A Declarer's Workbook

Exercise 19

Vul: N/S; Dealer: East

North
- ♠ A865
- ♥ KJ42
- ♦ A864
- ♣ 8

South
- ♠ K94
- ♥ A53
- ♦ K1053
- ♣ KJ6

East	South	West	North
P	1♦	P	1♥
P	1NT	P	3NT
All Pass			

Lead: ♣5. East plays the ♣Q and you win your King. Plan the play.

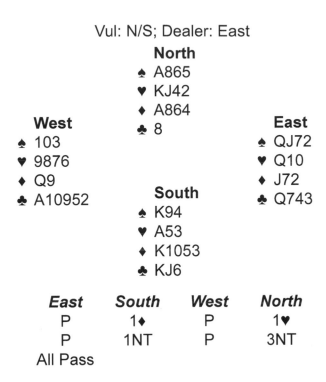

Vul: N/S; Dealer: East

North
♠ A865
♥ KJ42
♦ A864
♣ 8

West
♠ 103
♥ 9876
♦ Q9
♣ A10952

East
♠ QJ72
♥ Q10
♦ J72
♣ Q743

South
♠ K94
♥ A53
♦ K1053
♣ KJ6

East	South	West	North
P	1♦	P	1♥
P	1NT	P	3NT
All Pass			

Lead: ♣5. East plays the ♣Q and you win your King. Plan the play.

After the lead you have seven tricks. You only have one Club stopper and it is vulnerable to a Club lead from East. A Heart finesse means leading into the dangerous hand. Save that for last! You can set up a trick in either Spades or Diamonds by ducking a trick if the suit splits evenly. The chance of a 3–2 split in Diamonds is far better than a 3–3 split in Spades so attack Diamonds but keep East off lead. Lead to the ♦A and finesse the ♦10 unless East plays an honor. West might win but cannot attack Clubs. Your ♦K will now set up the ♦8 for your eighth trick. On a good day East will have the doubleton ♦QJ and you will score 4 Diamonds without a Heart finesse. You should be so lucky! Usually you will need to establish your ♥J. The best way is to lead low to the ♥K and back to the ♥A. If the lady has not fallen, lead up to the ♥J and hope for the best. This is better than a finesse through the ♥KJ because it also wins when East has the ♥Q singleton or doubleton. Take advantage of every chance.

Exercise 20

Vul: N/S; Dealer: South

North
- ♠ QJ5
- ♥ AJ92
- ♦ Q54
- ♣ KQ5

South
- ♠ K1074
- ♥ K104
- ♦ AK103
- ♣ A7

South	West	North	East
1NT	P	2♣	P
2♠	P	4NT[1]	P
6NT	All Pass		

1. Quantitative small slam try denying a Spade fit.

Lead: ♣J. Plan the play.

North
- ♠ QJ5
- ♥ AJ92
- ♦ Q54
- ♣ KQ5

West
- ♠ A93
- ♥ 86
- ♦ J872
- ♣ J1096

East
- ♠ 862
- ♥ Q753
- ♦ 96
- ♣ 8432

South
- ♠ K1074
- ♥ K104
- ♦ AK103
- ♣ A7

South	West	North	East
1NT	P	2♣	P
2♠	P	4NT[1]	P
6NT	All Pass		

1. Quantitative small slam try denying a Spade fit.

Lead: ♣J. Plan the play.

You have 11 tricks after losing the ♠A. Trick 12 must come from Hearts or Diamonds. Hearts offers a two-way finesse. *In general, put off two way finesses for as long as you can.* You should play the other winners in hopes of getting a count on each Opponent's hand. First try to develop another trick somewhere else. If you play 3 rounds of Diamonds one of two good things could happen. They might split 3–3 or the ♦J could fall in two rounds. Win the ♣A and drive out the ♠A. Win any return and play 3 rounds of Diamonds. If the ♦J falls your ♦10 is your twelfth trick. If not, play your remaining Spades and Clubs to learn what you can about distribution. On the configuration shown you will learn that West started with 3 Spades, 4 Diamonds and 3 to 5 Clubs. You will learn that there is more space in East's hand for the ♥Q than there is in West's. Run your Heart finesse through East. The lesson of this hand is that when you have an unavoidable two way guess, learn what you can about the distribution of the Opponents' cards by playing your winners. Make your decision based on what you have learned from the bidding and play.

Exercise 21

When you are in a trump contract holding a side suit AQJ10(x) opposite a small singleton you have a familiar problem in disguise: a two way finesse. You can take one standard finesse leading up to the AQ or you can take a ruffing finesse by leading small up to the Ace and then leading back to the void, using trump to capture the Opponent's hoped–for King. How do you choose? Particularly when there has been no bidding by the Opponents, your decision is often guided by factors outside the suit in question. How many tricks do you need in this side suit? Is there a dangerous hand to keep off lead?

Vul: None; Dealer: West

North
- ♠ A53
- ♥ Q64
- ♦ AQJ108
- ♣ 86

South
- ♠ 86
- ♥ AK975
- ♦ 5
- ♣ A7542

West	North	East	South
P	1♦	P	1♥
P	1NT	P	2♣¹
P	2♥²	P	4♥
All Pass			

1. *New Minor Forcing.*
2. *Three card Heart support.*

Lead: ♠K. Plan the play.

Vul: None; Dealer: West

North
♠ A53
♥ Q64
♦ AQJ108
♣ 86

West
♠ KQJ9
♥ 82
♦ K76
♣ J1093

East
♠ 10742
♥ J103
♦ 9432
♣ KQ

South
♠ 86
♥ AK975
♦ 5
♣ A7542

West	North	East	South
P	1♦	P	1♥
P	1NT	P	2♣¹
P	2♥²	P	4♥
All Pass			

1. *New Minor Forcing.*
2. *Three card Heart support.*

Lead: ♠K. Plan the play.

The lead of the ♠K removes a valuable Dummy entry. The Diamond suit is your source of tricks and you need an entry to Dummy after they are established. The only remaining entry is the ♥Q so trump better be 3–2 or Diamonds favorably split. It is sometimes right to lead up to the AQJ10 and take the finesse but not here. If that finesse loses you will lose a Spade trick. Instead play the ♦A followed by the ♦Q. If East plays the ♦K ruff it, draw trump ending in Dummy and play Diamonds for as long as you can, discarding your small Spade and low Clubs. If East does not cover the ♦Q discard your last Spade. West will win but you have a resting spot for two small Clubs and a third if Diamonds divide 3–4 or 4–3. In effect, playing the ♠6 under your ♦Q is a loser on loser play. The key play is taking the ruffing finesse discarding your last Spade instead of leading up to the ♦AQJ10. The problem with leading up to the Diamonds is that you do not get to pitch your losing Spade when taking the finesse. This is often the deciding factor in how to play this configuration of cards.

A Declarer's Workbook

Exercise 22

Vul: Both; Dealer: South
Scoring: IMPs

North
- ♠ K7
- ♥ A65
- ♦ K754
- ♣ K642

South
- ♠ A43
- ♥ KQ1032
- ♦ A82
- ♣ Q3

South	West	North	East
1♥	2NT¹	3♣²	P
4♥	All Pass		

1. *5–5 or better in the minors.*
2. *Invitational hand or better with Heart support.*

Lead: ♦Q. Plan the play.

Vul: Both; Dealer: South; Scoring: IMPs

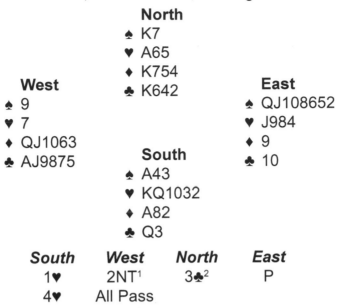

North
- ♠ K7
- ♥ A65
- ♦ K754
- ♣ K642

West
- ♠ 9
- ♥ 7
- ♦ QJ1063
- ♣ AJ9875

East
- ♠ QJ108652
- ♥ J984
- ♦ 9
- ♣ 10

South
- ♠ A43
- ♥ KQ1032
- ♦ A82
- ♣ Q3

South	West	North	East
1♥	2NT¹	3♣²	P
4♥	All Pass		

1. *5–5 or better in the minors.*
2. *Invitational hand or better with Heart support.*

Lead: ♦Q. Plan the play.

If you play for a quick Spade ruff at trick two you will make 5♥ most of the time. That IMP could make a difference. On this layout you will regret that choice and West's bidding gave you adequate warning. West will ruff the second Spade lead and you still have a possible Spade loser. If you ruff your remaining Spade loser you will not be able to make two trump leads to discover the Heart distribution and then take the finesse through East's ♥J. You will lose 100 instead of winning 620. The difference of 720 will cost your team 12 IMPs. You risked 12 IMPs in order to gain one. Why risk a large loss for a small gain? Instead, at trick two put the Spade ruff aside and make the prudent play of the ♥K and lead to the ♥A. If Hearts are 3–2 you can afford to ruff the third Spade because even if you get over-ruffed you were losing that third Spade anyway. On this layout you will discover the Heart distribution and be able to take the proven finesse through East. You will lose a Spade along with a Club and a Diamond, making your contract. At IMPS you play for overtricks only when you can do so without risking your contract. In this hand, if the defensive cards are very distributional (as West's 2NT bid suggests) you could go down. At IMPS do not risk a big plus score for an overtrick.

A Declarer's Workbook

Exercise 23

Vul: None; Dealer: South
Matchpoints

North
♠ 9743
♥ KQJ7
♦ 863
♣ 97

South
♠ Q8
♥ 84
♦ AKQ752
♣ K83

South	West	North	East
1♦	P	1♥	X
2♦	P	P	X
P	3♣	3♦	All Pass

Lead: ♣Q. East overtakes with the ♣A and returns the ♣2. Plan the play.

Vul: None; Dealer: South; Matchpoints

North
♠ 9743
♥ KQJ7
♦ 863
♣ 97

West
♠ K102
♥ 965
♦ J104
♣ QJ104

East
♠ AJ65
♥ A1032
♦ 9
♣ A652

South
♠ Q8
♥ 84
♦ AKQ752
♣ K83

South	West	North	East
1♦	P	1♥	X
2♦	P	P	X
P	3♣	3♦	All Pass

Lead: ♣Q. East overtakes with the ♣A and returns the ♣2. Plan the play.

If Diamonds are no worse than 3–1 you have eight tricks. You can ruff a Club in the short hand so 9 tricks should be easy. Can you score an overtrick by taking a minimal risk to your contract? Surely you can take one Heart trick but can you take two? Perhaps, but it depends on how East defends. East probably has the ♥A and one or both of the ♠AK. You could play the ♦AK and ruff a Club but wait. If you lead up to the ♥K immediately after winning the ♣K East will have no knowledge of where your strength lies. When East wins the ♥A the choice of what to lead might not be clear if East holds the ♠A or ♠K but not both. On the layout shown East gains by leading the ♠A but if the ♠K and ♠Q are swapped then East will have set up your (hypothetical) ♠K. If East does not lead the ♠A after winning the ♥A you will be able to get to dummy by drawing two rounds of trump, ruffing your last Club and then discarding a Spade on the ♥J. Playing the ♦AK at trick 3 tells East where the ♠K might lie, making a Spade shift easier to find. Usually we ruff in the short hand as soon as we can but sometimes we hold off a bit with relative safely to use that ruff as transportation to reach a trick that we have established.

Exercise 24

Vul: E/W; Dealer: East

North
- ♠ 87
- ♥ A75
- ♦ K7532
- ♣ AJ8

South
- ♠ AQ5
- ♥ K64
- ♦ A64
- ♣ K932

East	South	West	North
P	1NT	P	3NT
All Pass			

Lead: ♠6. East plays the ♠J and you win with the ♠Q. Plan the play.

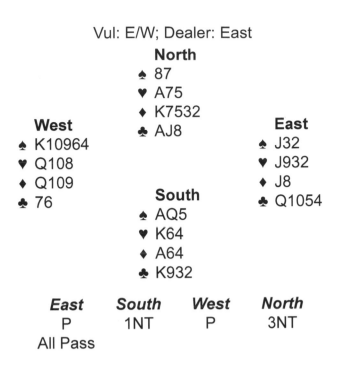

Vul: E/W; Dealer: East

North
- ♠ 87
- ♥ A75
- ♦ K7532
- ♣ AJ8

West
- ♠ K10964
- ♥ Q108
- ♦ Q109
- ♣ 76

East
- ♠ J32
- ♥ J932
- ♦ J8
- ♣ Q1054

South
- ♠ AQ5
- ♥ K64
- ♦ A64
- ♣ K932

East	South	West	North
P	1NT	P	3NT
All Pass			

Lead: ♠6. East plays the ♠J and you win with the ♠Q. Plan the play.

You have 8 top tricks and only one Spade stopper remaining. Your ninth trick has to be in one of the minors. In Diamonds you could win two extra tricks if they split 3–2. Setting up Diamond tricks requires you to lose at least one Diamond. If Diamonds are not 3–2 you could set up two defensive tricks if you start with the ♦A and ♦K and then play a small one. It is far better to play the ♦A. If Diamonds are 5–0, abandon Diamonds and try Clubs. If Diamonds are not 5–0, play a low Diamond and hope Diamonds are 3–2. But do you start Diamonds before Clubs? In Clubs you have a finesse with the ♣J and even if the finesse loses Clubs could split 3–3. Do not base your choice of the first suit to play on which single option is most likely to succeed. ***Choose the suit to play based on which suit gives you the most tricks. That is why you start with Diamonds.*** At trick 2 play the ♦A. If Diamonds are 5–0 test Clubs (either winning the finesse or Clubs being 3–3) saving your ♦K as a stopper. If Diamonds are not 5–0, duck a round of Diamonds to see if they are 3–2. If Diamonds are 4–1, win any return, cash the ♦K and test Clubs. If Diamonds are 3–2 win any return and run Diamonds. The third Club trick is not needed. By playing in this order you make your contract when either option works. Start with the option that keeps you alive.

A Declarer's Workbook

Exercise 25

Vul: E/W; Dealer: North
IMPs

North
- ♠ A7
- ♥ Q842
- ♦ KJ965
- ♣ 86

South
- ♠ K64
- ♥ AJ6
- ♦ A104
- ♣ A743

North	East	South	West
P	P	1NT	P
2♣	P	2♦	P
3NT	All Pass		

Lead: ♣K. East shows count with the 9. Plan the play.

North
♠ A7
♥ Q842
♦ KJ965
♣ 86

West
♠ 9532
♥ 93
♦ 72
♣ KQJ102

East
♠ QJ108
♥ K1075
♦ Q83
♣ 95

South
♠ K64
♥ AJ6
♦ A104
♣ A743

North	East	South	West
P	P	1NT	P
2♣	P	2♦	P
3NT	All Pass		

Lead: ♣K. East shows count with the 9. Plan the play.

The ♣K looks like the top of a sequence. You have 6 top tricks. Diamonds might supply the other 3. Taking the finesse into East will be safe if you duck Clubs until East has none. If the finesse fails you will be able to fall back on the Heart finesse. How many times do you duck? You and Dummy hold 6 Clubs. If West has 5 then East has 2. So you duck once before taking the Diamond finesse. If East has a third Club then West can only have 4 so you cannot be set by West running Clubs. You will still have a chance to take the Heart finesse. There is a formula to determine how many times to duck when you fear an opponent has enough tricks in a suit to set you: the Ducking Rule of 7. Count the number of cards Declarer and Dummy hold in the suit. Subtract that number from 7. The remainder tells you how many times to duck. On this hand $7 - 6 = 1$. Duck the first Club but win the second. By doing so you know that if East has a Club to return to West if the Diamond finesse fails then West will not have enough Clubs to set you. Because of IMP scoring Declarer's strategy should be to maximize the chance to get 9 tricks. This hand is much more complex at matchpoints because ducking twice gives a certain count on clubs, thereby increasing the chance of finding the ♦Q and winning overtricks.

Exercise 26

Vul: None; Dealer: West

North
- ♠ 85
- ♥ 108753
- ♦ AJ5
- ♣ KQ4

South
- ♠ A93
- ♥ A964
- ♦ K1086
- ♣ A9

West	North	East	South
P	P	P	1NT
P	2♦¹	P	2♥
P	3NT	P	4♥
All Pass			

1. *Transfer to Hearts.*

Lead: ♠K. Plan the play.

Vul: None; Dealer: West

North
- ♠ 85
- ♥ 108753
- ♦ AJ5
- ♣ KQ4

West
- ♠ KQJ2
- ♥ J
- ♦ 932
- ♣ J8732

East
- ♠ 10764
- ♥ KQ2
- ♦ Q74
- ♣ 1065

South
- ♠ A93
- ♥ A964
- ♦ K1086
- ♣ A9

West	North	East	South
P	P	P	1NT
P	2♦¹	P	2♥
P	3NT	P	4♥
All Pass			

1. Transfer to Hearts.

Lead: ♠K. Plan the play.

We have 8 weak trumps plus the Ace. Do we duck a trump trick and then win the Ace in order to keep a defender from drawing a trump from each hand? We have a Spade loser, a possible Diamond loser and 1, 2 or 3 trump losers depending on how trumps divide. If they are 2–2 we hold our losers to 1 by playing the Ace either first or second. If trump are 3–1 we are going to lose 2 trumps so we cannot afford to lose a Diamond. If West holds 4 trumps we cannot avoid 3 trump losers and our contract will fail. If East holds 4 trumps we can prevent a third trump loser by getting to Dummy with Clubs and leading the ♥10 from dummy and finessing if East does not cover. Whether the finesse wins or loses we play the ♥A on the second round of trump. This approach restricts our trump losers to 1 trick if trump are 2–2. If trump are 4–0 with East or 3–1 in either direction we are going to lose 2 trump tricks but you have an end play. Leave the high trump outstanding. Play all of the Clubs and ruff the Spade loser if that has not already been done. With no black cards in either hand give the defender who holds the high trump that trick. There is no safe exit.

A Declarer's Workbook

Exercise 27

Vul: N/S; Dealer: East

North
- ♠ 94
- ♥ Q95
- ♦ KJ7
- ♣ AJ753

South
- ♠ K8
- ♥ AJ106
- ♦ AQ65
- ♣ K106

East	South	West	North
P	1NT	2♠	3NT
All Pass			

Lead: ♠Q. East plays the ♠A followed by the 7 showing either a doubleton or an odd number of Spades. Plan the play.

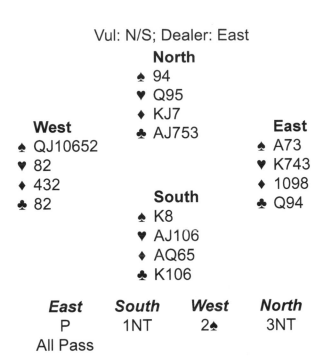

Vul: N/S; Dealer: East

North
- ♠ 94
- ♥ Q95
- ♦ KJ7
- ♣ AJ753

West
- ♠ QJ10652
- ♥ 82
- ♦ 432
- ♣ 82

East
- ♠ A73
- ♥ K743
- ♦ 1098
- ♣ Q94

South
- ♠ K8
- ♥ AJ106
- ♦ AQ65
- ♣ K106

East	South	West	North
P	1NT	2♠	3NT
All Pass			

Lead: ♠Q. East plays the ♠A followed by the 7 showing either a doubleton or an odd number of Spades. Plan the play.

East's ♠7 looks like the middle card from an original holding of three or the last card from a doubleton, leaving West with 6 or 7 Spades. You have 8 top tricks. East could hold the ♥K or ♣Q but if you take either finesse and it loses you are down if East started with 3 Spades. There is a much better play than an immediate finesse. You have 8 Clubs and 7 Hearts. Dropping a singleton or doubleton ♣Q is more likely than dropping a singleton ♥K. Start by taking your 4 Diamond tricks, pitching a Heart from dummy. Next play the ♣K and lead up to the ♣A. You retain the lead whether the ♣Q drops or not. If it does, you should run the Clubs to guarantee your contract. The Heart finesse would be optional. If the ♣Q does not fall the Heart finesse is necessary to take nine tricks. On the layout shown the Heart finesse wins. On a bad day the ♣Q will not fall and the Heart finesse will lose. But on a very good day the ♣Q will fall when the Heart finesse loses. You will make a game while others go down. That possibility is why we win the ♣K and ♣A before taking the Heart finesse.

A Declarer's Workbook

Exercise 28

Vul: Both; Dealer: North

North
- ♠ 9875
- ♥ KQ107
- ♦ A6
- ♣ K65

South
- ♠ 6
- ♥ AJ842
- ♦ K753
- ♣ Q43

North	East	South	West
1♣	P	1♥	1♠
2♥	2♠	4♥	All Pass

Lead: ♠A (Ace from AK) followed by the ♠Q. Plan the play.

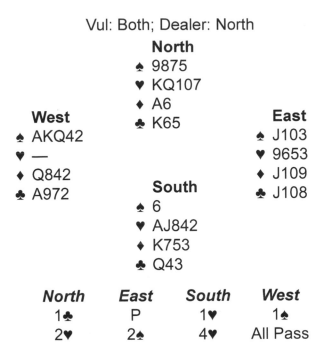

Vul: Both; Dealer: North

North
♠ 9875
♥ KQ107
♦ A6
♣ K65

West
♠ AKQ42
♥ —
♦ Q842
♣ A972

East
♠ J103
♥ 9653
♦ J109
♣ J108

South
♠ 6
♥ AJ842
♦ K753
♣ Q43

North	East	South	West
1♣	P	1♥	1♠
2♥	2♠	4♥	All Pass

Lead: ♠A (Ace from AK) followed by the ♠Q. Plan the play.

We know how to handle either a 2–2 or 3–1 trump split but what will we do if trump are 4–0? Ruff the ♠Q low and lead the ♥4 to the ♥10. We lead Hearts before Diamonds to check for a 4–0 break and change our strategy if necessary. When West shows a Heart void we must use one of Declarer's high Hearts to draw trump. We cannot afford to overtake it to get to Dummy. We need another entry to Dummy and the ♣K is our only option. We ruff a Spade with the ♥8 and lead the ♦3 to the ♦A. We make our third Spade ruff with the ♥J and play the ♥A to draw East's second trump. We lead up to the ♣K. If West has the ♣A we will get to Dummy either now or later with the ♣K and draw the remaining trump with the ♥K and ♥Q. We will then take our ♦K and concede the rest. Good players consider how to detect and deal with a 4–0 split at trick one. That is why we must draw a round of trump before leading Diamonds to get to Dummy.

Exercise 29

Vul: Both; Dealer: South

North
♠ Q63
♥ 762
♦ Q4
♣ KQJ52

South
♠ AKJ5
♥ A84
♦ A62
♣ 1063

South	*West*	*North*	*East*
1NT	P	3NT	All Pass

Lead: ♥5 (fourth best). Plan the play.

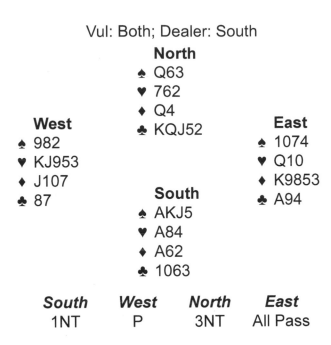

Vul: Both; Dealer: South

North
♠ Q63
♥ 762
♦ Q4
♣ KQJ52

West
♠ 982
♥ KJ953
♦ J107
♣ 87

East
♠ 1074
♥ Q10
♦ K9853
♣ A94

South
♠ AKJ5
♥ A84
♦ A62
♣ 1063

South	West	North	East
1NT	P	3NT	All Pass

Lead: ♥5 (fourth best). Plan the play.

You appear to have 10 tricks off the top once you drive out the ♣A. West found your weakness. If Hearts are 4–3 there is no problem. You can lose 3 Hearts and the ♣A and take 9 tricks. What if Hearts are 5–2 or 6–1? If so and West has the ♣A you have no chance so assume East has the ♣A. If West has 5 Hearts then East has 2 since your side holds 6. You can prevent East from getting to West in Spades and Diamonds after winning the ♣A. Most importantly you can run East out of Hearts by ducking the first trick. When East returns a Heart it will be the last one. When East wins the presumed ♣A there will be no way to put West in the lead before you cash your winners. When you see the Heart lead you must consider the various distributions of Hearts to determine how East can be prevented from leading a Heart to West after driving out your ♥A. Ducking one round of Hearts will do it when Hearts are 5–2. Can you simplify things by just ducking until you have to play the ♥A? If you do that West will recognize that there is no future in Hearts and in desperation lead the ♦J. Your ♦A will be driven out and East will cash the Diamonds after winning the ♣A. Figure out how many times you need to duck and do so, but not one trick more! The ducking rule of 7 says to subtract the number of cards you hold in the suit (6) from 7 yielding 1.

A Declarer's Workbook

Exercise 30

Vul: None; Dealer: West

North
- ♠ 9832
- ♥ A3
- ♦ AQ3
- ♣ Q743

South
- ♠ KQJ54
- ♥ 75
- ♦ 64
- ♣ AK95

West	North	East	South
P	1♣	P	1♠
P	2♠	P	4♠
All Pass			

Lead: ♥K. Plan the play.

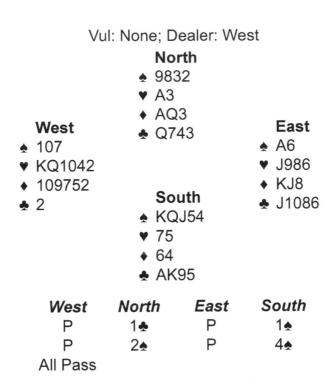

Vul: None; Dealer: West

North
♠ 9832
♥ A3
♦ AQ3
♣ Q743

West
♠ 107
♥ KQ1042
♦ 109752
♣ 2

East
♠ A6
♥ J986
♦ KJ8
♣ J1086

South
♠ KQJ54
♥ 75
♦ 64
♣ AK95

West	North	East	South
P	1♣	P	1♠
P	2♠	P	4♠
All Pass			

Lead: ♥K. Plan the play.

This hand seems easy. Ask yourself what could go wrong. You have losers in Spades and Hearts and a possible loser in Diamonds. If Clubs are 4–1 or 5–0 (about 1/3 of the time) you have a Club loser. Can we avoid the Diamond finesse? If the Clubs are to your left you cannot. However, if the Clubs are to your right you have an end play possibility. The time to plan for this is at the opening lead. Waiting until you find out about the bad Club split will be too late. If you win the ♥A on trick one, draw trump and then start the Clubs and find the bad split everyone at the table will see what is happening. When you lead your small Heart West will win and will immediately find the switch to a small Diamond forcing you to guess. That switch is much harder to find if you duck the first Heart. West might look for a Club ruff or continue Hearts. If West does anything but lead a Diamond at trick two you will be able to end play East on the fourth Club. If West finds the Diamond shift at trick two, compliment the defense and move on. You did what you could.

Exercise 31

Vul: Both; Dealer: West

North
♠ K742
♥ 85
♦ AJ2
♣ AK109

South
♠ AJ1085
♥ A4
♦ Q64
♣ 432

West	North	East	South
2♥[1]	X	3♥	4♠
All Pass			

1. Preemptive

Lead: ♥K. Plan the play.

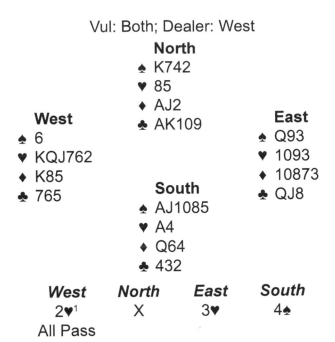

Vul: Both; Dealer: West

North
♠ K742
♥ 85
♦ AJ2
♣ AK109

West
♠ 6
♥ KQJ762
♦ K85
♣ 765

East
♠ Q93
♥ 1093
♦ 10873
♣ QJ8

South
♠ AJ1085
♥ A4
♦ Q64
♣ 432

West	*North*	*East*	*South*
2♥[1]	X	3♥	4♠
All Pass			

1. Preemptive

Lead: ♥K. Plan the play.

You start with three likely losers: one each in Hearts, Diamonds and Clubs. You must find the ♠Q. Should you rely on "Eight Ever, Nine Never?" Not on your life!! The bidding tells you that West has 6 Hearts while East has only 3. Put another way, West has 7 cards that are not Hearts while East has 10. Neither Opponent needs the ♠Q for their bid. Based on what you know, the odds strongly favor the ♠Q sitting with East. The play that has the best chance of success is to lead low to the ♠K in case someone has a stiff ♠Q. If the ♠Q did not fall lead up to the ♠J. This is a much better strategy than playing for the drop just because you have nine Spades. Remember, Eight Ever, Nine Never should be used only when you have no information about the Opponents' hands or an Opponent to keep off lead. That is not the case here. One more point. By ducking trick 1 you might be able to end play East and avoid the Diamond finesse. West will likely continue Hearts and that clears your Heart suit. After trump are drawn play Clubs. On the layout shown East will have no safe exit after winning the third Club. East will be forced to lead a Diamond or give you a ruff and discard. You will then be able to pitch a Diamond on Dummy's fourth Club.

A Declarer's Workbook

Exercise 32

Vul: N/S; Dealer: South

North
- ♠ A83
- ♥ A1084
- ♦ KQJ6
- ♣ 92

South
- ♠ 754
- ♥ KJ95
- ♦ A95
- ♣ A76

South	West	North	East
1♣	1♠	X	P
2♥	P	4♥	All Pass

Lead: ♠K. East plays the ♠J. What next?

Vul: N/S; Dealer: South

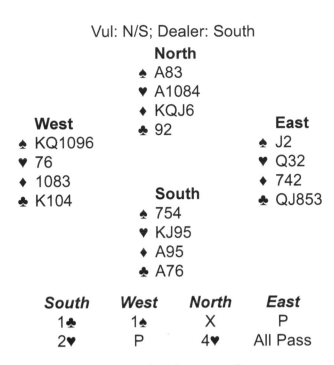

North
- ♠ A83
- ♥ A1084
- ♦ KQJ6
- ♣ 92

West
- ♠ KQ1096
- ♥ 76
- ♦ 1083
- ♣ K104

East
- ♠ J2
- ♥ Q32
- ♦ 742
- ♣ QJ853

South
- ♠ 754
- ♥ KJ95
- ♦ A95
- ♣ A76

South	West	North	East
1♣	1♠	X	P
2♥	P	4♥	All Pass

Lead: ♠K. East plays the ♠J. What next?

You start with 1 Club loser, 2 possible losers in Spades and 1 in Hearts. Since West's 1♠ bid could be made with as little as 8 HCP West does not necessarily hold the ♥Q. The Heart finesse is a guess. West probably has 5 Spades since the overcall was not 2♠. Thus, East probably has 2 Spades. Whether you take the first or second Spade, if you take the Heart finesse into West and it loses you will lose a total of two Spades because you have not yet pitched Declarer's third Spade. What happens if you take the Heart finesse into East? If you win the first Spade East will still have a Spade to return to West and you will lose two Spade tricks. If you duck the first Spade, win the second and then take the Heart finesse into East there will be no way for East to get to West because East will have no more Spades and you control the other suits. You can draw trump and then run Diamonds to drop Dummy's third Spade. Ducking the first Spade severs communication between West and East. If you then take the Heart finesse into East you will survive whether the finesse wins or not. Avoiding defeat if the Heart finesse loses is the key. ***You must plan for a losing Heart finesse before playing to trick one.***

A Declarer's Workbook

Exercise 33

Vul: None; Dealer: South

North
- ♠ AQ87
- ♥ 942
- ♦ AK2
- ♣ 652

South
- ♠ 543
- ♥ K3
- ♦ Q865
- ♣ AKQ3

South	West	North	East
1♦	1♥	X	P
1NT	P	3NT	All Pass

Lead: ♠9. Plan the play.

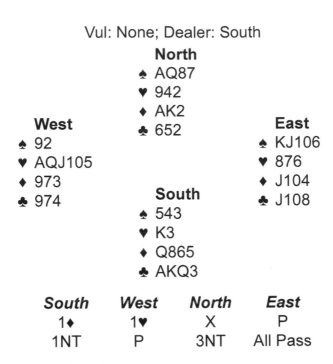

Vul: None; Dealer: South

North
- ♠ AQ87
- ♥ 942
- ♦ AK2
- ♣ 652

West
- ♠ 92
- ♥ AQJ105
- ♦ 973
- ♣ 974

East
- ♠ KJ106
- ♥ 876
- ♦ J104
- ♣ J108

South
- ♠ 543
- ♥ K3
- ♦ Q865
- ♣ AKQ3

South	West	North	East
1♦	1♥	X	P
1NT	P	3NT	All Pass

Lead: ♠9. Plan the play.

You are wide open to a Heart lead from your right. West's ♠9 looks like an attempt to get to East for a Heart lead. If you play the ♠Q and East has the ♠K then a Heart will surely be coming back and down you go. Why risk the Spade finesse at trick 1 if you can get to 9 tricks another way? If both Clubs and Diamonds are 3–3 you do not need a second Spade trick. Moreover, if West has the ♠K and was hoping to find the ♠A or ♠Q with East he will still have the ♠K after you test the minors. Win the ♠A immediately and test the minor suits. If both split 3–3 you will have 9 tricks and it will be safe to lead up to the ♠Q for an overtrick. If either or both of the minor suits fail to split evenly then take all of the top tricks that you can (to minimize the damages) and lead up to the ♠Q. If only one of the minor suits was 3–3 you will have 8 tricks. If West has the ♠K it will be the last non-Heart in West's hand. West will be forced to concede a trick to your ♥K. If East has the ♠K you will take no more tricks but will have minimized the damage.

Exercise 34

Vul: N/S; Dealer: West

North
- ♠ AK65
- ♥ 86
- ♦ 1093
- ♣ AQ107

South
- ♠ Q42
- ♥ A74
- ♦ AQJ6
- ♣ 853

West	North	East	South
P	1♣	1♥	3NT
All Pass			

Lead: ♥2 (low from three small). Plan the play.

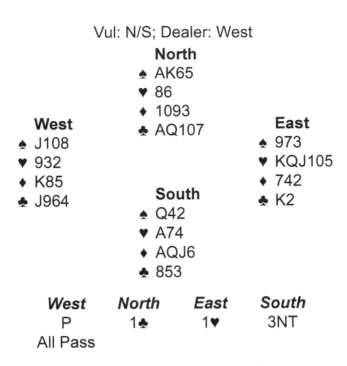

Vul: N/S; Dealer: West

North
♠ AK65
♥ 86
♦ 1093
♣ AQ107

West
♠ J108
♥ 932
♦ K85
♣ J964

East
♠ 973
♥ KQJ105
♦ 742
♣ K2

South
♠ Q42
♥ A74
♦ AQJ6
♣ 853

West	North	East	South
P	1♣	1♥	3NT
All Pass			

Lead: ♥2 (low from three small). Plan the play.

You have 6 tricks. You need 3 more. The Diamond finesse goes into West. How many Hearts does East have? Check the vulnerability. West is a Passed hand. Expect East to bid with any excuse. A solid 5 card suit is possible, leaving West with 3 Hearts. You can duck Hearts twice. If you do so you have chances to make your contract even if the Diamond finesse fails, no matter how many Hearts East has but there is another trap. If you take the Diamond finesse before testing Spades and the finesse loses, what will you play if West leads a Club? You do not know if you need the Club finesse or not. Before playing Diamonds lead 2 rounds of Spades starting with the ♠Q. If both Opponents follow play your last Spade honor. If Spades are 3–3 you do not need the Club finesse. You have 9 tricks even if the Diamond finesse fails. If Spades are not 3–3 you need either the Diamond or Club finesse to win. If the Diamond finesse loses, West could cash a winning Spade but that only gives the defense 4 tricks. Now the Club finesse is necessary. If it loses, c'est la vie. The key plays are ducking Hearts twice and testing Spades before taking the Diamond finesse.

Exercise 35

Vul: None; Dealer: East

North
- ♠ 7652
- ♥ K6
- ♦ K84
- ♣ A1064

South
- ♠ K843
- ♥ AQ52
- ♦ AQ5
- ♣ 83

East	South	West	North
P	1NT	2♣	X[1]
P	2♥	P	3NT
P	4♠	All Pass	

1. Stayman.

Lead: ♣K. Plan the play.

Vul: None; Dealer: East

North
- ♠ 7652
- ♥ K6
- ♦ K84
- ♣ A1064

West
- ♠ AQ
- ♥ 983
- ♦ 1096
- ♣ KQJ75

East
- ♠ J109
- ♥ J1074
- ♦ J732
- ♣ 92

South
- ♠ K843
- ♥ AQ52
- ♦ AQ5
- ♣ 83

East	South	West	North
P	1NT	2♣	X[1]
P	2♥	P	3NT
P	4♠	All Pass	

1. Stayman.

Lead: ♣K. Plan the play.

Nice auction but this will be a test. You have a Club loser and 2 or 3 Spade losers. Based on the bidding West likely has the ♠A. If West has 3 Spades including the Ace or if trump are 4–1 or 5–0 in either direction you have no chance. What configuration of the cards gives you a chance? If West holds the ♠Ax you can force the play of the Ace without using your ♠K. Win the ♣A and duck a Spade into West. West will take the ♠Q and likely take a Club and shift to a red suit. Win the trick in either hand and play low trump from both hands. If West had a doubleton Ace it will fall. Your ♠K can now draw the remaining trump and ten tricks are yours. No bidding errors were made. Sometimes the texture of your trump suit will be weak even when the number of trump and overall high card strength are correct. When that happens consider the possible layouts of the defense's cards that will allow you to succeed. In this hand you need either Opponent to have a doubleton ♠A. Ducking two Spades into West holds your trump losers to two and you make your contract.

A Declarer's Workbook

Exercise 36

Vul: N/S; Dealer: South
Scoring: IMPs

North
- ♠ K7
- ♥ A65
- ♦ K754
- ♣ K642

South
- ♠ A43
- ♥ KQ1032
- ♦ A82
- ♣ Q3

South	West	North	East
1♥	P	2♣¹	P
2♦	P	4♥	All Pass

1. Game forcing.

Lead: ♦9. Plan the play.

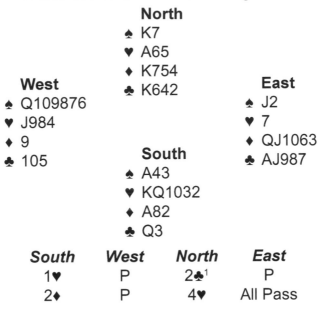

North
- ♠ K7
- ♥ A65
- ♦ K754
- ♣ K642

West
- ♠ Q109876
- ♥ J984
- ♦ 9
- ♣ 105

East
- ♠ J2
- ♥ 7
- ♦ QJ1063
- ♣ AJ987

South
- ♠ A43
- ♥ KQ1032
- ♦ A82
- ♣ Q3

South	West	North	East
1♥	P	2♣[1]	P
2♦	P	4♥	All Pass

1. Game forcing.

Lead: ♦9. Plan the play.

Do not feel too sorry for yourself because the Hearts are 4–1 with the Jxxx behind you. That is going to happen now and then with an 8 card trump fit. With that split you have a trump loser in addition to the Club and Diamond losers. What you cannot afford is a second trump loser but that is what will result on this layout if you try for a Spade ruff before testing Hearts. Start by winning the ♦A on trick 1 so that it will not be ruffed on the second Diamond lead if West led a singleton. Make the normal play of the ♥K followed by the ♥A. Now you know the Heart layout even if you do not know how Spades are divided. When you lead the third Spade East will not have a trump to overruff and you are safe. What happens if West is the defender who is short in Spades? West gains nothing by ruffing your third Spade high because that gives up the natural trump trick. Likewise, ruffing a Diamond does not help the defense because you can duck in Dummy. Notice that on this hand the eleventh trick you were hoping for is a mirage. Focus on making 10 tricks at IMPs. At IMPs ask yourself "What could go wrong?" and protect yourself if possible. At Matchpoints ask yourself "Is there a relatively safe way to get an overtrick or two?" and play accordingly. The strategies are very different and a good Declarer knows that.

Exercise 37

Vul: Both; Dealer: South

North
♠ 73
♥ KQ872
♦ 64
♣ AJ54

South
♠ 85
♥ AJ543
♦ A95
♣ K106

South	West	North	East
1♥	P	2NT[1]	P
4♥[2]	All Pass		

1. Game force with 4+ card support.
2. Minimum opening hand.

Lead: ♦3. Plan the play.

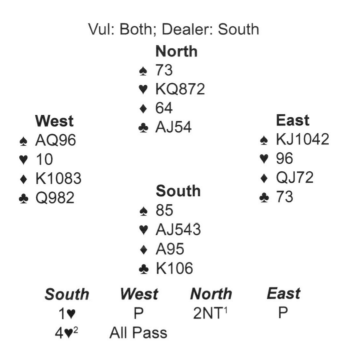

Vul: Both; Dealer: South

North
- ♠ 73
- ♥ KQ872
- ♦ 64
- ♣ AJ54

West
- ♠ AQ96
- ♥ 10
- ♦ K1083
- ♣ Q982

East
- ♠ KJ1042
- ♥ 96
- ♦ QJ72
- ♣ 73

South
- ♠ 85
- ♥ AJ543
- ♦ A95
- ♣ K106

South	West	North	East
1♥	P	2NT[1]	P
4♥[2]	All Pass		

1. Game force with 4+ card support.
2. Minimum opening hand.

Lead: ♦3. Plan the play.

You must lose 2 Spades and a Diamond. You cannot afford a Club loser. You can avoid the Club guess by making the Opponents lead Clubs. There are two factors to guide you: lots of trump and an equal number of losing Spades in both hands – basic ingredients for a strip and end play. You want either Opponent on lead when the only cards left in the North and South hands are trump and Clubs. Then they have to lead you a Club or give you a ruff and discard. There's one key play. It comes at trick one. After trick one you want to draw trump, trump South's last Diamond in Dummy and then throw the Opponents in by leading a Spade. If you win the first trick you cannot do that. The Opponents will be able to escape by leading a third round of Diamonds and forcing you to ruff. But if you duck trick one, you can win the second Diamond and ruff North's third Diamond before giving up the lead in Spades. It is true that East could scuttle these plans by shifting to a Spade at trick two but that is a pretty tough defense to find unless East holds the ♠AK. Few Easts will even consider a Spade lead at trick two from ♠KJ10xx. Fewer still will actually make the shift.

Exercise 38

Vul: None; Dealer: East

North
- ♠ J874
- ♥ 6
- ♦ K873
- ♣ K952

South
- ♠ AKQ32
- ♥ 8743
- ♦ A4
- ♣ 64

East	South	West	North
1♥	1♠	2♥	3♥[1]
X	4♠	All Pass	

1. Limit raise in Spades.

Lead: ♥J overtaken by East's ♥Q. East leads the ♠5. Plan the play.

Vul: None; Dealer: East

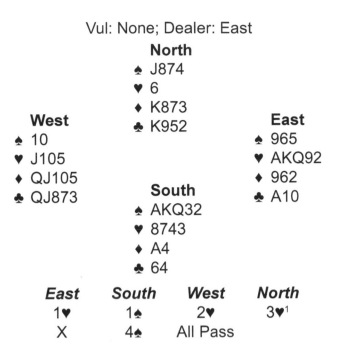

North
♠ J874
♥ 6
♦ K873
♣ K952

West
♠ 10
♥ J105
♦ QJ105
♣ QJ873

East
♠ 965
♥ AKQ92
♦ 962
♣ A10

South
♠ AKQ32
♥ 8743
♦ A4
♣ 64

East	South	West	North
1♥	1♠	2♥	3♥[1]
X	4♠	All Pass	

1. Limit raise in Spades.

Lead: ♥J overtaken by East's ♥Q. East leads the ♠5. Plan the play.

With 7 tricks and a possible eighth in Clubs the obvious place to turn is ruffing Hearts in Dummy so Dummy's trump must be used wisely. East did well to shift to a trump. There are few entries to Declarer's hand outside of trump. Win East's trump lead in hand and ruff a Heart. Return to the South hand by leading to the ♦A in order to trump another Heart. The last entry to South's hand outside of trump would be trumping a Diamond after winning the ♦K. Is this worth the risk of an overruff? The risk is small but even if it happens nothing is lost. If Declarer cannot ruff that last Heart it will be a loser. It is better to take the risk of the overruff in order to avoid a certain Heart loser. Next problem: how to get back to South's hand after the last Heart ruff. Lead a Diamond. If East shows out it is safe to ruff low or to overruff. If East has a Diamond then ruff high and play the remaining high Spade. If Spades were 2–2 South can lead up to the ♣K. If Spades were 3–1 you will lose a trump trick but you avoided a Heart loser. Ruffing in the long hand was for transportation, not to create a trick. Ruffing 3 Hearts in Dummy – the short hand – created 3 tricks.

A Declarer's Workbook

Exercise 39

Vul: Both; Dealer: East

North
- ♠ A532
- ♥ 852
- ♦ A9
- ♣ Q1072

South
- ♠ KQ6
- ♥ AK4
- ♦ 10753
- ♣ KJ9

East	South	West	North
P	1NT	P	2♣
P	2♦	P	3NT

All Pass

Lead: ♦4 (fourth best). Plan the play.

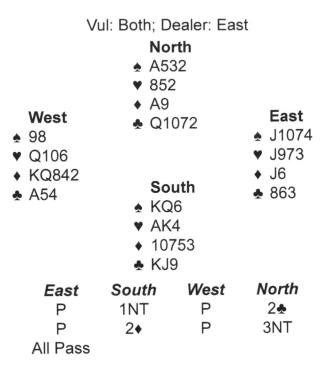

Vul: Both; Dealer: East

North
- ♠ A532
- ♥ 852
- ♦ A9
- ♣ Q1072

West
- ♠ 98
- ♥ Q106
- ♦ KQ842
- ♣ A54

East
- ♠ J1074
- ♥ J973
- ♦ J6
- ♣ 863

South
- ♠ KQ6
- ♥ AK4
- ♦ 10753
- ♣ KJ9

East	South	West	North
P	1NT	P	2♣
P	2♦	P	3NT
All Pass			

Lead: ♦4 (fourth best). Plan the play.

You have 6 Diamonds between you and Dummy so this looks like a ducking play to run East out of Diamonds. Are the ♦KQJ with West? If so, West would have led the ♦K. East must have a Diamond honor doubleton if Diamonds are 5–2. Look at your Diamond spots. If you duck a Diamond East will play his honor and return a Diamond. West will play low because your ♦A must fall. If West has the ♣A his ♦KQ will draw your Diamonds and defeat you. Instead, rise with the ♦A and immediately attack Clubs preserving the ♠A as an entry. If East wins the ♣A he will lead the ♦J. West must overtake to gain the lead because he has no other entries and your ♦10 becomes a stopper. If West has the ♣A he must play the ♦K, crushing East's ♦J and establishing your ♦10 as a stopper. The lesson here is to look carefully at the opening lead and your spots in the suit. 10s, 9s and 8s can sometimes become secondary stoppers. Just because they lead a long suit do not duck automatically. There is a broader lesson here. When you hold the Ace of a suit but are missing the KQJ take note of the first lead. If they do not lead the K their partner almost always has one of the top honors because the standard lead from KQJx(x..) is the K, not small. The same logic applies when you hold the AK and they hold the QJ10.

Exercise 40

Vul: N/S; Dealer: West

North
- ♠ AJ72
- ♥ 107
- ♦ J64
- ♣ KQJ5

South
- ♠ K10543
- ♥ A652
- ♦ K5
- ♣ A7

West	North	East	South
P	1♣	2♥	2♠
P	3♠	P	4♠
All Pass			

Lead: ♥8. East covers with the ♥J. Plan the play (1) for IMPs and (2) for Matchpoints.

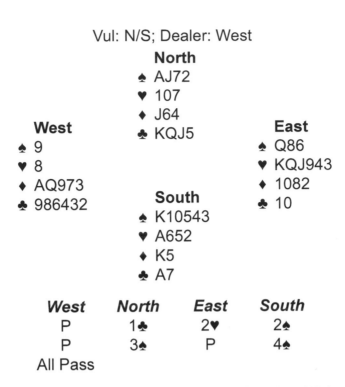

Vul: N/S; Dealer: West

North
♠ AJ72
♥ 107
♦ J64
♣ KQJ5

West
♠ 9
♥ 8
♦ AQ973
♣ 986432

East
♠ Q86
♥ KQJ943
♦ 1082
♣ 10

South
♠ K10543
♥ A652
♦ K5
♣ A7

West	North	East	South
P	1♣	2♥	2♠
P	3♠	P	4♠
All Pass			

Lead: ♥8. East covers with the ♥J. Plan the play (1) for IMPs and (2) for Matchpoints.

You have 1 Heart loser plus 2 possible Diamond losers and 1 in Spades. The auction makes West more likely than East to hold the ♠Q. You will be able to dump both of your Diamonds on Clubs as soon as trumps are drawn. At IMPs you are willing to give up an overtrick to guarantee your contract, giving up 1 IMP to guarantee 12. You must prevent East from leading a Diamond. Win the ♥A, lead to the ♠A (to drop a stiff ♠Q) and lead the ♠J to finesse East. Do not finesse West or play for the drop. West will probably win but cannot attack your ♦K. Finessing East guaranties 10 tricks. Matchpoints strategy is very different. Since West is a favorite to hold the ♠Q you usually avoid a trump loser if you finesse West, not East. Finessing East will lose most of the time. Making 10 tricks when others are making 11 will get you a poor result at matchpoints. Risking your contract at Matchpoints by finessing West is a good play. On this layout it loses, but it is still the right play because it will win far more often than not and get you an overtrick and a good score.

A Declarer's Workbook

Exercise 41

Vul: None; Dealer: East

North
- ♠ 85
- ♥ AQ104
- ♦ 853
- ♣ KJ52

South
- ♠ KJ6
- ♥ 95
- ♦ AK104
- ♣ AQ74

East	South	West	North
P	1NT	P	2♣
P	2♦	P	3NT
All Pass			

Lead: ♠3 (fourth best leads) to East's ♠Q and Declarer's ♠K. What now?

Vul: None; Dealer: East

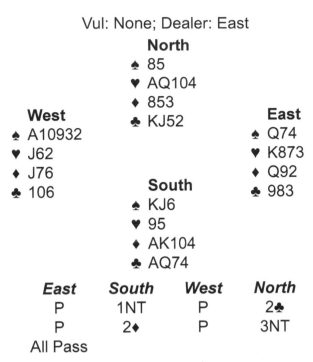

North
♠ 85
♥ AQ104
♦ 853
♣ KJ52

West
♠ A10932
♥ J62
♦ J76
♣ 106

East
♠ Q74
♥ K873
♦ Q92
♣ 983

South
♠ KJ6
♥ 95
♦ AK104
♣ AQ74

East	South	West	North
P	1NT	P	2♣
P	2♦	P	3NT
All Pass			

Lead: ♠3 (fourth best leads) to East's ♠Q and Declarer's ♠K.
What now?

You have eight top tricks. You could start with the Heart finesse but
if it loses a Spade is coming back and that would be a disaster if
Spades are 5–3 and that seems likely since you have not seen the ♠2.
Diamonds offer hope but if you start with the ♦A and ♦K you have
no control over who wins the third Diamond. If East wins disaster
is certain. Instead go to Dummy with a Club to lead a Diamond,
intending to finesse the ♦10 unless the ♦Q or ♦J appears. West's best
defense is a Heart. Since you cannot allow East to win you must
play the ♥A. Play your ♦A and ♦K to see if your ninth trick is your
♦4. If not, run the Clubs and lead up to the ♥Q. If it loses to East
you are going down but you gave yourself two chances. If the ♦Q
or ♦J appeared when you led the ♦3 you must cover but what next?
Get to Dummy with another Club and lead another Diamond. If the
other Diamond honor appears your ♦10 is now good. There is not
much chance of a doubleton ♦QJ to your right but that unlikely lie of
the cards, together with 3–3 Diamonds plus the Heart finesse gives
you a great chance of success. The Diamond finesse is an avoidance
play, a common necessity as part of a "combining" strategy.

A Declarer's Workbook

Exercise 42

Vul: N/S; Dealer: North

North
- ♠ A76
- ♥ K64
- ♦ J9743
- ♣ A6

South
- ♠ K84
- ♥ Q8532
- ♦ AQ10
- ♣ K3

North	East	South	West
1♦	2♣	2♥	P
3♥	P	4♥	All Pass

Lead: ♣9. Plan the play.

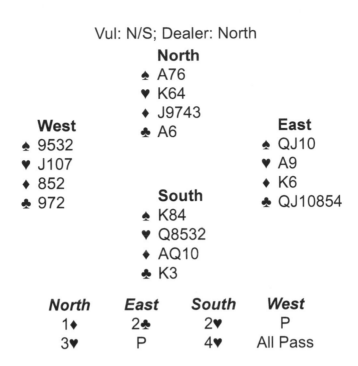

Vul: N/S; Dealer: North

North
♠ A76
♥ K64
♦ J9743
♣ A6

West
♠ 9532
♥ J107
♦ 852
♣ 972

East
♠ QJ10
♥ A9
♦ K6
♣ QJ10854

South
♠ K84
♥ Q8532
♦ AQ10
♣ K3

North	East	South	West
1♦	2♣	2♥	P
3♥	P	4♥	All Pass

Lead: ♣9. Plan the play.

You have a Spade loser, a possible Diamond loser and 1 or 2 trump losers. Preserve a Dummy entry to start the Diamond finesses but if the ♦K is offside your contract will depend on losing only 1 trump. How can you do that when missing the Ace, Jack 10 and 9? If trump are not 3–2 you cannot. If they are 3–2 you can hold your trump losers to 1 by leading through the Ace and then ducking a trick on the way back, hoping the Ace was doubleton. You can lead up to either Heart honor. Which do you choose? East's 2♣ bid shows 5+ Clubs and the great majority of the outstanding strength. The ♥A is almost certainly with East and it might be doubleton. The best play is to lead up to the ♥Q after winning the opening lead with the ♣A. While finding the ♥A with East is highly likely you will be fortunate if it is doubleton – it could be singleton or East might have 3 or more. If the ♥Q wins, lead a Heart to Dummy and *duck*. This is called an obligatory finesse. If the Ace falls on air you have made your contract by listening to the bidding and being a little lucky. Your ♥K will capture the last trump and the Diamond finesse is for an overtrick. Even if the ♥A does not fall you still can try the Diamond finesse. You have given yourself two chances to make 4♥.

A Declarer's Workbook

Exercise 43

Vul: None; Dealer: West

North
- ♠ AQ5
- ♥ K986
- ♦ 985
- ♣ Q86

South
- ♠ K43
- ♥ AJ1042
- ♦ J10
- ♣ KJ4

West	North	East	South
P	P	P	1♥
P	3♥[1]	P	4♥
All Pass			

1. Four card limit raise.

Lead: West leads the ♦A (Ace from AK), continues with the ♦K, shifts to the ♣A and then shifts to the ♠8 when East plays the ♣3 under West's Ace. Plan the play.

Vul: None; Dealer: West

North
♠ AQ5
♥ K986
♦ 985
♣ Q86

West
♠ 8762
♥ 5
♦ AK73
♣ A952

East
♠ J109
♥ Q73
♦ Q642
♣ 1073

South
♠ K43
♥ AJ1042
♦ J10
♣ KJ4

West	North	East	South
P	P	P	1♥
P	3♥¹	P	4♥
All Pass			

1. Four card limit raise.

Lead: West leads the ♦A (Ace from AK), continues with the ♦K, shifts to the ♣A and then shifts to the ♠8 when East plays the ♣3 under West's Ace. Plan the play.

"Eight Ever, Nine Never" says to play for the drop of the Queen but think for a second. Have you been counting West's hand? West has already played an Ace–King and an Ace. With the ♥Q West surely would have opened the bidding. You know East must have the ♥Q. Play the ♥K. If the ♥Q does not appear, finesse the ♥9. Finish drawing trump and claim. The lead of the ♣A by West gave us a count of high card points. It broadcast that all the rest of the defensive high cards rested with East since West did not open the bidding. There are no running side suits so the ♣A was not going away. West should shift to Spades immediately after winning the ♦K and force Declarer to figure out trump for himself. Even so, Opponents make mistakes and we need to take advantage of them!!

Exercise 44

Vul: Both; Dealer: East

North
- ♠ 954
- ♥ 84
- ♦ A1075
- ♣ AK95

South
- ♠ 63
- ♥ KQJ953
- ♦ K8
- ♣ QJ6

East	South	West	North
1♦	1♥	P	P
1♠	2♥	2♠	4♥
All Pass			

Lead: ♠J followed by the ♠2 to East's ♠Q and ♠K, which you ruff in hand. Plan the play.

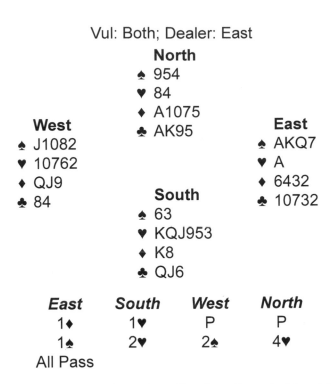

Vul: Both; Dealer: East

North
♠ 954
♥ 84
♦ A1075
♣ AK95

West
♠ J1082
♥ 10762
♦ QJ9
♣ 84

East
♠ AKQ7
♥ A
♦ 6432
♣ 10732

South
♠ 63
♥ KQJ953
♦ K8
♣ QJ6

East	South	West	North
1♦	1♥	P	P
1♠	2♥	2♠	4♥
All Pass			

Lead: ♠J followed by the ♠2 to East's ♠Q and ♠K, which you ruff in hand. Plan the play.

You have lost two Spades and will lose the ♥A but everything looks solid. This looks like an excellent 23 point vulnerable game. Your teammates will be thrilled. If you get careless and start drawing trump by placing the ♥K on the table, your teammates will no longer be thrilled because you just set yourself in a cold contract. *Always become a pessimist when things look easy.* What can go wrong here is East having a stiff ♥A and West having four to the 10. On the bidding that is certainly a possibility. The solution is easy once you see the danger. Cross to Dummy in your shorter minor suit, Diamonds, to lead up to your Hearts. When East's singleton Ace appears you retain the KQJ to draw West's remaining trump. When trying to establish running honors it is often good technique to lead up to them rather than leading them. Sometimes a singleton Ace will appear or a defender will err and you can save an honor for later.

A Declarer's Workbook

Exercise 45

Vul: Both; Dealer: East

North
- ♠ 105
- ♥ 7543
- ♦ AKQ6
- ♣ 953

South
- ♠ 864
- ♥ AKQ
- ♦ 84
- ♣ AK1042

East	South	West	North
P	1NT	P	2♣
P	2♦	P	3NT
All Pass			

Lead: ♠K. West continues Spades. East wins the fourth Spade and shifts to the ♣8. Plan the play.

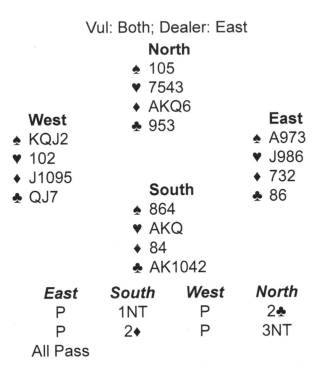

Vul: Both; Dealer: East

North
♠ 105
♥ 7543
♦ AKQ6
♣ 953

West
♠ KQJ2
♥ 102
♦ J1095
♣ QJ7

East
♠ A973
♥ J986
♦ 732
♣ 86

South
♠ 864
♥ AKQ
♦ 84
♣ AK1042

East	South	West	North
P	1NT	P	2♣
P	2♦	P	3NT
All Pass			

Lead: ♠K. West continues Spades. East wins the fourth Spade and shifts to the ♣8. Plan the play.

You will want to run Dummy's Hearts or Diamonds later so discard Clubs on the last two Spades. It might seem that this hand requires Hearts to be 3–3 or the ♣QJ to be doubleton. There is a good additional chance. Win the ♣A and play three rounds of Hearts. If Hearts are 3–3 Dummy's fourth Heart is good. If not, it is likely that one of the opponents must protect both minors. If the Hearts are not 3–3 one of the Opponents will have eight or more cards in the Majors leaving little room for the minors. Your third Heart is the eighth trick (4 Spades, 1 Club and 3 Hearts). On the layout shown West can no longer protect both minors. A discard from either suit sets up that suit for Declarer. Regardless of what West discards on the ♥Q cash the ♣K. If the ♣Q and ♣J fall cash the Clubs and Diamonds. If the Clubs are not good play Dummy's Diamonds. The fourth one will usually set up. Notice that swapping the West and East hands makes no difference. An opponent protecting both minors must yield one of those suits on trick 8. Notice also that West holding even more minor suit cards will not help. At trick 8 West will come down to 4 Diamonds and 2 Clubs and have to discard one of them.

A Declarer's Workbook

Exercise 46

Vul: N/S; Dealer: North

North
- ♠ KJ943
- ♥ 985
- ♦ 875
- ♣ A6

South
- ♠ 752
- ♥ AK6
- ♦ AQJ6
- ♣ K94

North	East	South	West
P	P	1NT	P
2♥¹	P	2♠	P
2NT	P	4♠	All Pass

1. Transfer to Spades.

Lead: ♣Q. Plan the play.

Vul: N/S; Dealer: North

North
- ♠ KJ943
- ♥ 985
- ♦ 875
- ♣ A6

West
- ♠ 108
- ♥ J1072
- ♦ 1094
- ♣ QJ105

East
- ♠ AQ6
- ♥ Q43
- ♦ K32
- ♣ 8732

South
- ♠ 752
- ♥ AK6
- ♦ AQJ6
- ♣ K94

North	East	South	West
P	P	1NT	P
2♥¹	P	2♠	P
2NT	P	4♠	All Pass

1. Transfer to Spades.

Lead: ♣Q. Plan the play.

You have a sure Heart loser and a possible Diamond loser. Even if trump are 3–2 you have 1 to 3 trump losers. You have a finesse in Diamonds and a double finesse in trump. You need two of those three to work so how do you start? The key play is that your first trump finesse must be the 9, not the K or J, unless West plays a higher card. If the 9 loses to the 10, come back to hand and finesse the J unless West plays a higher card. If the 9 loses to the A then you know where the Q and 10 are and you have them surrounded with Dummy's KJ. If the 9 loses to the Q then Dummy's KJ will capture West's 10. What do you do when the 9 loses and East returns a Diamond? If the 9 lost to anything lower than the A you will have 2 trump losers so the Diamond finesse must work for you to succeed. If the 9 loses to the A then you can hold your trump losers to 1 so the Diamond finesse is for an overtrick. At IMPs you must consider that East's Diamond could be a singleton and you cannot afford to let East ruff a Diamond with a low trump. Scorn the finesse. At Matchpoints take the finesse, since East's Diamond is rarely a stiff.

Exercise 47

Vul: E/W; Dealer: North

North
- ♠ 752
- ♥ KQ872
- ♦ 742
- ♣ 86

South
- ♠ A864
- ♥ A53
- ♦ A6
- ♣ A932

North	East	South	West
P	P	1NT	P
2♦¹	P	2♥	All Pass

1. Transfer to Hearts.

Lead: ♦K. Plan the play.

Vul: E/W; Dealer: North

North
♠ 752
♥ KQ872
♦ 742
♣ 86

West
♠ Q9
♥ J1094
♦ KQJ8
♣ J75

East
♠ KJ103
♥ 6
♦ 10953
♣ KQ104

South
♠ A864
♥ A53
♦ A6
♣ A932

North	East	South	West
P	P	1NT	P
2♦¹	P	2♥	All Pass

1. Transfer to Hearts.

Lead: ♦K. Plan the play.

There are 8 tricks as long as Hearts are 3–2. If Hearts break badly there is a trump loser or two that cannot be helped. Usually ruffing in the short hand is done in the Dummy. In No Trump auctions Declarer often holds fewer trumps after a transfer, making Declarer's the "short" hand. Given that hint, look closely at this example. Declarer can ruff Dummy's third Diamond in hand before drawing all of the trumps. The result will be 6 trump tricks instead of 5 if trump are 3–2. This yields an overtrick, which at Matchpoints is important. Even at teams, an extra IMP cannot hurt. The big payoff comes when trumps break badly, as they will about a third of the time. With a 4–1 split you win only 4 trump tricks and go down one unless you win that early Diamond ruff. With trump 5–0 you gain by going down only 1 instead of 2. Best play is to win the ♦A and shoot a Diamond right back. Declarer wins any return and gets to Dummy with a low trump to the ♥K. After ruffing Dummy's last Diamond Declarer plays the ♥A and the ♣A and ♣2 to get back to Dummy with a Club ruff to finish drawing trump.

Exercise 48

Vul: None; Dealer: East

North
- ♠ AQ2
- ♥ AJ5
- ♦ J874
- ♣ 952

South
- ♠ 973
- ♥ K1083
- ♦ AKQ3
- ♣ K7

East	South	West	North
P	1NT	P	3NT
All Pass			

Lead: ♣Q. Plan the play.

Vul: None; Dealer: East

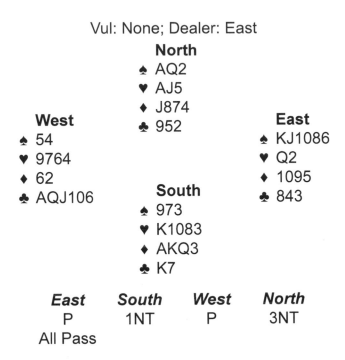

North
- ♠ AQ2
- ♥ AJ5
- ♦ J874
- ♣ 952

West
- ♠ 54
- ♥ 9764
- ♦ 62
- ♣ AQJ106

East
- ♠ KJ1086
- ♥ Q2
- ♦ 1095
- ♣ 843

South
- ♠ 973
- ♥ K1083
- ♦ AKQ3
- ♣ K7

East	*South*	*West*	*North*
P	1NT	P	3NT
All Pass			

Lead: ♣Q. Plan the play.

You start with 8 tricks – an all too familiar theme. You have two possible finesses; one in Spades and a two-way finesse in Hearts. Whichever finesse you choose, if it loses the Opponents will be playing Clubs for a while. You cannot afford to lose the lead, so how can you do better than a 50/50 finesse? Lead up to the ♥A and then back to the ♥K. The ♥Q will sometimes fall and your Hearts will all be good. There is a small chance of this but you will not lose the lead if it fails so why not try it? You can try the Spade finesse later if you need to. Your chance of success increases so it is surely a good play. There is one more thing to consider before leading a Heart. West's ♣Q lead shows Club length. Therefore the ♥Q is likely with East. Lead low to the ♥A and back with the ♥J, not the ♥5. Many East players will automatically cover with the ♥Q if they have it. You were not going to take that finesse but East might not figure that out. Give East a chance to err. Particularly if East holds the ♥Q9xx the correct action when the ♥J is led is not obvious. Giving an Opponent the chance to err is a valid part of a "combining" strategy. Experts do it all the time. So should you.

A Declarer's Workbook

Exercise 49

Vul: None; Dealer: North

North
- ♠ A3
- ♥ K742
- ♦ AJ983
- ♣ 94

South
- ♠ 842
- ♥ AQ53
- ♦ K1065
- ♣ K8

North	East	South	West
1♦	P	1♥	P
2♥	P	4♥	All Pass

Lead: ♠Q. Plan the play.

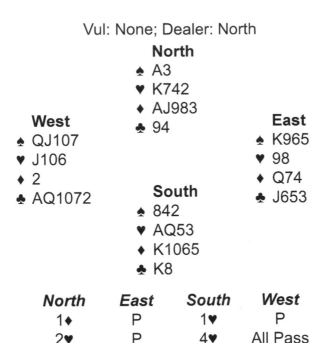

Vul: None; Dealer: North

North
- ♠ A3
- ♥ K742
- ♦ AJ983
- ♣ 94

West
- ♠ QJ107
- ♥ J106
- ♦ 2
- ♣ AQ1072

East
- ♠ K965
- ♥ 98
- ♦ Q74
- ♣ J653

South
- ♠ 842
- ♥ AQ53
- ♦ K1065
- ♣ K8

North	East	South	West
1♦	P	1♥	P
2♥	P	4♥	All Pass

Lead: ♠Q. Plan the play.

If Hearts split 3–2 you lose 1 Spade, perhaps 1 Diamond and 1 or 2 Clubs. Danger lurks in Clubs. Do you win trick 1? Who has the ♠K? West's lead says it is East, the danger hand. If you win trick 1, West can get to East with a Spade for a Club switch that will be obvious. If you duck, East must overtake and switch to Clubs at once. That is hard to see at trick 1. Win the second Spade, draw trump and set up Diamonds keeping East off lead. Lead a low Diamond to the Ace and finesse the ♦J. If that finesse loses, West cannot attack Clubs. The danger in Clubs dictates how to play Diamonds as long as Hearts are 3–2. Hearts will be 4–1 about 1/4 of the time. If that happens you have a Heart loser so you must not lose a Diamond. Finding the ♦Q becomes more important than keeping East off lead. Draw 3 rounds of trump and leave the high trump out. Place the ♦Q with the player who is short in Hearts. If that means West, so be it. The trump loser forces you to maximize your chance of capturing the ♦Q. If you do, a losing Club will go on Dummy's fifth Diamond. You will lose 1 Spade, 1 Heart and 1 Club. If East has 4 Hearts and West has the ♣Ax(xx) you cannot make the hand against competent defense.

Exercise 50

Vul: N/S; Dealer: West

North
- ♠ 7
- ♥ A872
- ♦ A865
- ♣ KQ72

South
- ♠ A93
- ♥ 9654
- ♦ KQ42
- ♣ A4

West	North	East	South
P	1♦	P	1♥
P	2♥	P	4♥
All Pass			

Lead: ♠K. Plan the play.

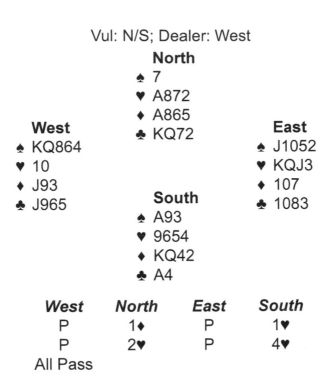

Vul: N/S; Dealer: West

North
♠ 7
♥ A872
♦ A865
♣ KQ72

West
♠ KQ864
♥ 10
♦ J93
♣ J965

East
♠ J1052
♥ KQJ3
♦ 107
♣ 1083

South
♠ A93
♥ 9654
♦ KQ42
♣ A4

West	North	East	South
P	1♦	P	1♥
P	2♥	P	4♥
All Pass			

Lead: ♠K. Plan the play.

If trump are 3–2 you have no problem but sometimes trump will be 4–1. If you win the ♠A and lead to the ♥A you could get quite a surprise when you make the second lead of trump. One of the Opponents could hold the ♥KQJ, draw your trump and then lead Spades. You can protect yourself by ducking a small trump on the first trump lead. This costs nothing. You are going to lose 2 trump tricks anyway. When you regain the lead play your ♥A. If both Opponents follow then there is a single high trump outstanding. You can claim 11 tricks. But if one of the Opponents shows out you have two high trumps outstanding but *you retain the lead.* Play the ♣A, ruff a Spade and cash your two top Clubs, discarding your last Spade. Continue to play your outside winners until a high trump is played. Now you have more trump than they do so they cannot draw your trump. You can claim 10 tricks in spite of the 4–1 trump split. Your only losers are the three trumps.

A Declarer's Workbook

Exercise 51

Vul: None; Dealer: South

North
- ♠ A10874
- ♥ K10
- ♦ KJ5
- ♣ A75

South
- ♠ QJ962
- ♥ AQ
- ♦ A1073
- ♣ K4

South	West	North	East
1♠	P	2NT[1]	P
3♠[2]	P	4♣[3]	P
4♦[4]	P	4NT[5]	P
5♠[6]	P	6♠	All Pass

1. Game force with 4+ trump.
2. Extra values
3. ♣ Control.
4. ♦ Control.
5. RKC 1430.
6. 2 or 5 Key Cards with ♠Q.

Lead: ♣Q. Plan the play.

Vul: None; Dealer: South

North
♠ A10874
♥ K10
♦ KJ5
♣ A75

West
♠ 3
♥ J974
♦ 964
♣ QJ1063

East
♠ K5
♥ 86532
♦ Q82
♣ 982

South
♠ QJ962
♥ AQ
♦ A1073
♣ K4

South	West	North	East
1♠	P	2NT¹	P
3♠²	P	4♣³	P
4♦⁴	P	4NT⁵	P
5♣⁶	P	6♠	All Pass

1. Game force with 4+ trump.
2. Extra values
3. ♣ Control.
4. ♦ Control.
5. RKC 1430.
6. 2 or 5 Key Cards with ♠Q.

Lead: ♣Q. Plan the play.

If either the Spade or Diamond finesse works you make your slam. That is about 75% but you can do better. The book play considering the Spades in isolation is to hook the ♠Q but that is not best on this hand. Notice the two way finesse in Diamonds, extra trump in both hands and that the Club and Heart suits can be eliminated from both hands. These are the ingredients for a strip and end play. Win the ♣Q in your hand and lead the ♠Q. Play the ♠A whether West covers or not. If the ♠K has appeared you are now playing for an overtrick. Draw trump and finesse for the ♦Q in the direction indicated by the defensive card count. If the ♠K does not drop *let it be.* Play your ♣A, ruff a Club and win the Heart tricks. Now a Spade lead endplays whoever holds the ♠K. This approach works whenever Spades are 2–1 and neither Opponent has a singleton or void in Hearts or Clubs. It also works if Spades are 3–0 if you find the ♦Q. The Spade void makes that Opponent more likely to hold the ♦Q, so the chance of avoiding a Diamond loser is pretty good.

A Declarer's Workbook

Exercise 52

Vul: Both; Dealer: South

North
- ♠ K92
- ♥ AKQ
- ♦ A9753
- ♣ 82

South
- ♠ AQJ10864
- ♥ 954
- ♦ 6
- ♣ AQ

South	West	North	East
1♠	P	2♦¹	P
2♠	P	3♠²	P
4♣³	P	4NT⁴	P
5♠⁵	P	7♠	All Pass

1. Game forcing.
2. Spade support with slam interest.
3. Club control.
4. Roman Key Card Blackwood.
5. 2 Key Cards plus the ♠Q.

Lead: ♠5. Plan the play.

Vul: Both; Dealer: South

North
- ♠ K92
- ♥ AKQ
- ♦ A9753
- ♣ 82

West
- ♠ 5
- ♥ J872
- ♦ Q842
- ♣ K1096

East
- ♠ 73
- ♥ 1063
- ♦ KJ10
- ♣ J7543

South
- ♠ AQJ10864
- ♥ 954
- ♦ 6
- ♣ AQ

South	West	North	East
1♠	P	2♦¹	P
2♠	P	3♠²	P
4♣³	P	4NT⁴	P
5♠⁵	P	7♠	All Pass

1. Game forcing.
2. Spade support with slam interest.
3. Club control.
4. Roman Key Card Blackwood.
5. 2 Key Cards plus the ♠Q.

Lead: ♠5. Plan the play.

At first glance this looks like a 50% grand slam. What else is there but the Club finesse? The answer is that Dummy's 5 card Diamond suit might give you a resting spot for the ♣Q. There are seven outstanding Diamonds. They will split 4–3 an amazing 62% of the time. You have enough entries to Dummy to ruff out the Diamonds. If they are 4–3 your ♣Q goes on the ♦3 and the Club finesse is not needed. If Diamonds do not behave you can still take the Club finesse. Needing either 4–3 Diamonds or the ♣K onside gives you two chances instead of one, always a good thing. The lesson here is that a 5–1 side suit with enough entries to the long hand can be the source of the trick you need to pitch a loser, whether to make your contract or to score the overtrick that will get you a top board at Matchpoints. Make sure a 5–1 side suit is part of your "combining" tool kit.

A Declarer's Workbook

Exercise 53

Vul: E/W; Dealer: West

North
- ♠ 8643
- ♥ AQ10
- ♦ AK853
- ♣ 6

South
- ♠ 7
- ♥ KJ743
- ♦ QJ4
- ♣ K753

West	North	East	South
P	1♦	1♠	2♥
2♠	4♥	All Pass	

Lead: ♠J. East wins the ♠Q and shifts to the ♣2. Plan the play.

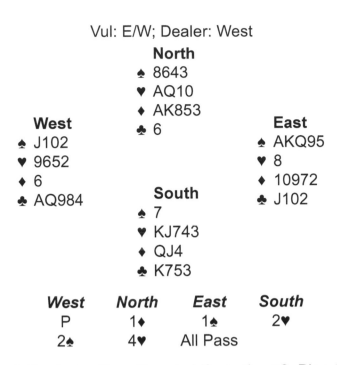

Vul: E/W; Dealer: West

North
♠ 8643
♥ AQ10
♦ AK853
♣ 6

West
♠ J102
♥ 9652
♦ 6
♣ AQ984

East
♠ AKQ95
♥ 8
♦ 10972
♣ J102

South
♠ 7
♥ KJ743
♦ QJ4
♣ K753

West	North	East	South
P	1♦	1♠	2♥
2♠	4♥	All Pass	

Lead: ♠J. East wins the ♠Q and shifts to the ♣2. Plan the play.

We have been studying Dummy Reversals and this hand looks like another. You have shortness in the long hand, high trump and outside entries in the short hand but there is something else that is more important. Your Diamonds look to be a running 5 card suit just like your trumps. Barring a wild distribution in the red suits you have 10 running tricks. If both Opponents follow to the first round of trump you can safely ruff a Club in Dummy for 11 tricks. What can be gained by using Dummy's high trump or high Diamonds to ruff Spades in South's hand? In the layout shown an attempt at a Dummy Reversal will likely give West an undeserved trump trick. The lesson here is that a Dummy Reversal rarely makes sense when either hand has what looks to be a running side suit. Remember that a Dummy Reversal is a technique for creating tricks by ruffing several tricks in the long hand. There is a risk of encountering unbalanced defensive holdings. This risk should only be taken when those extra tricks from the long hand are necessary. It rarely makes sense to risk a safe contract with a Dummy Reversal.

A Declarer's Workbook

Exercise 54

Vul: None; Dealer: East
Scoring: IMPs

North
- ♠ AK42
- ♥ A73
- ♦ 86
- ♣ 10732

South
- ♠ Q105
- ♥ Q92
- ♦ K4
- ♣ AKQJ9

East	South	West	North
P	1NT	P	2♣
P	2♦	P	3NT
All Pass			

Lead: ♥5. Plan the play.

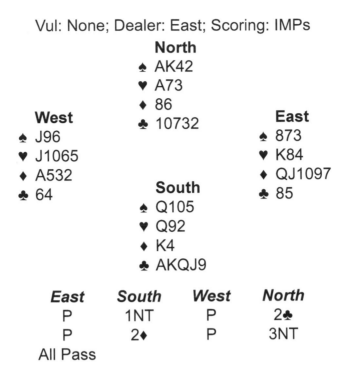

Vul: None; Dealer: East; Scoring: IMPs

North
- ♠ AK42
- ♥ A73
- ♦ 86
- ♣ 10732

West
- ♠ J96
- ♥ J1065
- ♦ A532
- ♣ 64

East
- ♠ 873
- ♥ K84
- ♦ QJ1097
- ♣ 85

South
- ♠ Q105
- ♥ Q92
- ♦ K4
- ♣ AKQJ9

East	South	West	North
P	1NT	P	2♣
P	2♦	P	3NT
All Pass			

Lead: ♥5. Plan the play.

We have seen these North and South hands before. You have 9 tricks off the top and the lead gives you a chance for a guaranteed tenth. The ♥5 certainly looks like a fourth-best lead so playing for the ♥K to your left might work. The only problem is that if the ♥K is to your right and the ♦A is to your left, a Diamond lead at trick two could doom your contract. What should you do at IMPs? Even though winning a tenth trick by ducking is a strong favorite you win only one additional IMP by doing so. If the ♥K is with East and the ♦A is with West you stand to lose five Diamond tricks if you duck the Heart lead. If that happens, you will turn a +400 into a –100, a loss of 11 IMPs. Ducking the Heart lead risks 11 IMPs to win 1. This is exceedingly poor strategy at IMPs. Go up with the ♥A. Take your nine top tricks. If Spades are 3–3 your fourth Spade will be a winner. Finally, lead up to the ♥Q. If the ♥K is to your left you might get an eleventh trick. Most importantly, you make game no matter how the defensive cards lie – the primary goal at IMPs. At IMPs risking your contract to score an overtrick is almost never right. That is not so at matchpoints.

A Declarer's Workbook

Exercise 55

Vul: E/W; Dealer: West

North
- ♠ 9863
- ♥ 5
- ♦ AKQJ
- ♣ KJ74

South
- ♠ A5
- ♥ AJ94
- ♦ 8643
- ♣ Q106

West	North	East	South
1♥	X	P	2NT
P	3NT	All Pass	

Lead: ♥K. East plays the ♥2 (standard signals). Plan the play.

Vul: E/W; Dealer: West

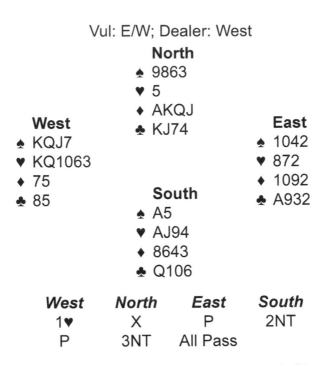

North
- ♠ 9863
- ♥ 5
- ♦ AKQJ
- ♣ KJ74

West
- ♠ KQJ7
- ♥ KQ1063
- ♦ 75
- ♣ 85

East
- ♠ 1042
- ♥ 872
- ♦ 1092
- ♣ A932

South
- ♠ A5
- ♥ AJ94
- ♦ 8643
- ♣ Q106

West	North	East	South
1♥	X	P	2NT
P	3NT	All Pass	

Lead: ♥K. East plays the ♥2 (standard signals). Plan the play.

On first glance it might appear that ducking a Heart or two makes sense. After all, the Ducking Rule of 7 tells you to duck Hearts twice. That would be a mistake. Look carefully at the Heart spots. Even if East gets in with the ♣A and leads a Heart West cannot run Hearts. West will see East's ♥2 discouraging signal and see there is no future in Hearts. If you duck West will likely shift to a Spade. If that happens your contract will fail because the defense will win three Spades, one Heart and one Club. This outcome can be prevented by winning the ♥K and immediately driving out the ♣A. No matter who has it and what they lead you cannot be prevented from winning four Diamonds, three Clubs, one Heart and one Spade. Ducking is a useful tool when protecting a suit that the defense might be able to run. That is not the case on this hand because of your Heart holding. Before choosing to duck a trick consider what might happen if the defense shifts to another suit. On this hand disaster awaits if you duck the opening lead.

Exercise 56

Vul: Both; Dealer: East

North
- ♠ 7
- ♥ KJ53
- ♦ K8432
- ♣ 843

South
- ♠ 9642
- ♥ AQ1074
- ♦ A9
- ♣ K6

East	South	West	North
1♠	2♥	2♠	3♥
All Pass			

Lead: ♠Q. East plays the ♠3 (standard signals). West continues with the ♥2. Plan the play.

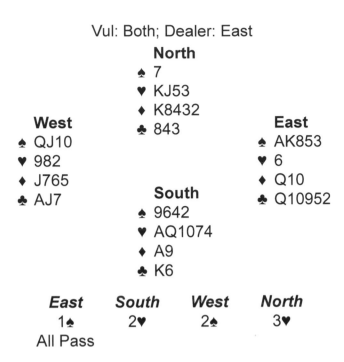

Vul: Both; Dealer: East

North
- ♠ 7
- ♥ KJ53
- ♦ K8432
- ♣ 843

West
- ♠ QJ10
- ♥ 982
- ♦ J765
- ♣ AJ7

East
- ♠ AK853
- ♥ 6
- ♦ Q10
- ♣ Q10952

South
- ♠ 9642
- ♥ AQ1074
- ♦ A9
- ♣ K6

East	South	West	North
1♠	2♥	2♠	3♥
All Pass			

Lead: ♠Q. East plays the ♠3 (standard signals). West continues with the ♥2. Plan the play.

Many East players would have carried on to 3♠ but this one failed to do so. The significance of this is that making your contract is the primary consideration even at matchpoints. You start with 7 tricks but need 9. Maybe leading up to the ♣K will add a trick but there is a better choice: ruffing Spades in Dummy. Win the ♥A and ruff a Spade. Return to your hand with the ♦A to ruff another Spade. Your two ruffs in Dummy are the tricks you need to make your contract so at IMPs you want to play it safe. Draw trump and take your 9 tricks ending with the ♦K. You will still be able to lead up to the ♣K for a possible overtrick. At Matchpoints you might try for another Spade ruff by cashing the ♦K and ruffing a Diamond high to get back to your hand to ruff a third Spade. That play risks your contract if the ♦K gets ruffed but making that extra trick figures to earn a top or close to it. As long as Diamonds are no worse than 4–2 you will be safe. It is a better than a 50/50 bet but on this hand that risk is unwise. You are in a contract that figures to be well above average because most East players will have carried on to 3♠. Why risk an above average score for a top when going down could get you a poor score?

Exercise 57

Vul: Both; Dealer: South

North
♠ 75
♥ KQ6
♦ KQ4
♣ AJ1062

South
♠ J32
♥ AJ95
♦ A
♣ Q8743

South	West	North	East
1♣	P	2♣¹	P
2♦²	P	2♥³	P
3♣⁴	P	5♣⁵	All Pass

1. *Limit raise or better denying a 4 card Major.*
2. *Diamond stopper.*
3. *Heart stopper.*
4. *No Spade stopper and a minimum hand.*
5. *Extras but no Spade stopper.*

Lead: ♠A followed by the ♠6 to the ♠Q and then the ♠K, which you ruff on the board. Plan the play.

Vul: Both; Dealer: South

North
- ♠ 75
- ♥ KQ6
- ♦ KQ4
- ♣ AJ1062

West
- ♠ A96
- ♥ 10732
- ♦ 9762
- ♣ K9

East
- ♠ KQ1084
- ♥ 84
- ♦ J10853
- ♣ 5

South
- ♠ J32
- ♥ AJ95
- ♦ A
- ♣ Q8743

South	West	North	East
1♣	P	2♣¹	P
2♦²	P	2♥³	P
3♣⁴	P	5♣⁵	All Pass

1. Limit raise or better denying a 4 card Major.
2. Diamond stopper.
3. Heart stopper.
4. No Spade stopper and a
   minimum hand.
5. Extras but no Spade
   stopper.

Lead: ♠A followed by the ♠6 to the ♠Q and then the ♠K, which you ruff on the board. Plan the play.

Nice auction. All you have to do is find the ♣K. Do you bang down the ♣A and play for the drop or do you take the finesse? You have no information from the bidding and, since you and partner hold 27 HCP the opponents hold 13. The first 3 tricks show 4 HCP to your left and 5 to your right. West does not have the length to overcall Spades and East cannot have the strength to overcall 2♠. Conclusion: the ♣K could be in either hand. Some players think playing for the drop has the better chance when holding 10 trump. This is wrong. The finesse is a 50% chance. Playing for the drop works only when Clubs are 2–1 *and* the ♣K is singleton. Since both of these things have to happen, the chance of success is about 26%. Since 50% is greater than 26% the correct play is the finesse. It only works 50% of the time but it is far better than 26%.

A Declarer's Workbook

Exercise 58

Vul: None; Dealer: South

North
- ♠ QJ5
- ♥ KJ95
- ♦ Q2
- ♣ Q875

South
- ♠ A1074
- ♥ A103
- ♦ K74
- ♣ AJ2

South	West	North	East
1NT	P	2♣	P
2♠	P	3NT	All Pass

Lead: ♦6. East/West are playing standard signals. Plan the play.

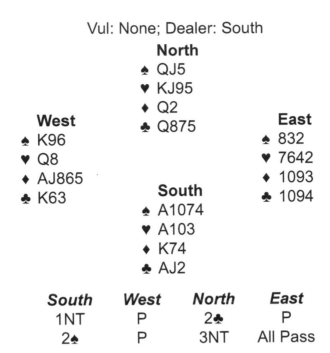

Vul: None; Dealer: South

North
- ♠ QJ5
- ♥ KJ95
- ♦ Q2
- ♣ Q875

West
- ♠ K96
- ♥ Q8
- ♦ AJ865
- ♣ K63

East
- ♠ 832
- ♥ 7642
- ♦ 1093
- ♣ 1094

South
- ♠ A1074
- ♥ A103
- ♦ K74
- ♣ AJ2

South	*West*	*North*	*East*
1NT	P	2♣	P
2♠	P	3NT	All Pass

Lead: ♦6. East/West are playing standard signals. Plan the play.

Do you play the ♦Q? If you duck it can be crushed by the Ace on the next Diamond lead. Play it now. If West has the Ace your ♦K can act as a second stopper. East plays the ♦3 under your ♦Q showing odd count. It looks like West started with five Diamonds to the Ace so we have to keep East off lead. You might want to use the ♥A and ♥K for a combining play later. Start with Spades but be careful to preserve entries to Dummy. Finesse the ♠Q. If it wins, lead the ♠5 to preserve the ♠J as an entry. West wins the ♠K and returns a Spade or a Diamond. If it is a Spade, get back to the board with the ♠J to finesse the ♥J. West wins and returns a small Heart. Play out your Major suits ending in Dummy and you will have taken 3 Spades, 3 Hearts and a Diamond. Lead a Club to finesse the Q. If it wins you are home. If not, West will be forced to lead either a Club or Diamond giving you the ninth trick. What happens if West defends by leading a low Diamond after winning the ♠K, thereby preserving communication with East? If this happens win your King and play your ♥A and ♥K. If the ♥Q falls you have 9 tricks. If not, take the Club finesse or end play West with a Diamond, your last chance.

Exercise 59

Vul: None; Dealer: North

North
- ♠ 7653
- ♥ 42
- ♦ AK3
- ♣ AK95

South
- ♠ K984
- ♥ AK7
- ♦ 82
- ♣ Q643

North	East	South	West
1♣	P	1♠	P
2♠	P	4♠	All Pass

Lead: ♥Q. Plan the play.

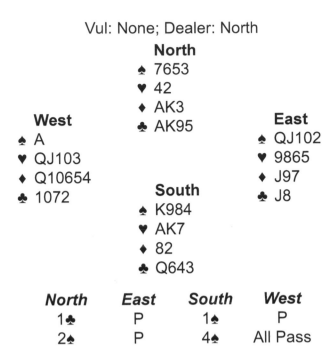

Vul: None; Dealer: North

North
- ♠ 7653
- ♥ 42
- ♦ AK3
- ♣ AK95

West
- ♠ A
- ♥ QJ103
- ♦ Q10654
- ♣ 1072

East
- ♠ QJ102
- ♥ 9865
- ♦ J97
- ♣ J8

South
- ♠ K984
- ♥ AK7
- ♦ 82
- ♣ Q643

North	East	South	West
1♣	P	1♠	P
2♠	P	4♠	All Pass

Lead: ♥Q. Plan the play.

This is one scary trump suit but do not panic. You are a strong favor-ite if you play this right! If trump are 3–2 you can draw trump los-ing only 3 tricks. If trump are 4–1 the ♠A will be onside half the time. You go down only when trump are 5–0 or the ♠A is offside and trump are 4–1 to your left. You can protect yourself from a 4–1 split and the ♠A being singleton by ducking the first lead of trump. You are going to lose a trump trick at some point. Lose it on the first trump and the possible singleton ♠A will go on air. Assuming Clubs behave you will succeed a great majority of the time using proper play. You doom yourself to failure by not drawing trump. If you play your outside winners without drawing trump someone is going to score a low trump. They will still hold their high trump and you will likely lose three additional trump tricks. As dangerous as it seems, you must win the ♥A and immediately play a low trump from each hand. If the ♠A has not appeared, get to Dummy with a Diamond (the shorter side suit) and lead up to the ♠K (unless East now plays the ♠A). On the layout shown you go down if you lead a low trump to the ♠K on the first play of trump. Ducking a round of trump is the key play!

Exercise 60

Vul: Both; Dealer: South

North
- ♠ A64
- ♥ 54
- ♦ AK964
- ♣ 986

South
- ♠ K3
- ♥ A986
- ♦ 853
- ♣ AKJ10

South	*West*	*North*	*East*
1NT	P	3NT	All Pass

Lead: ♠Q. Plan the play.

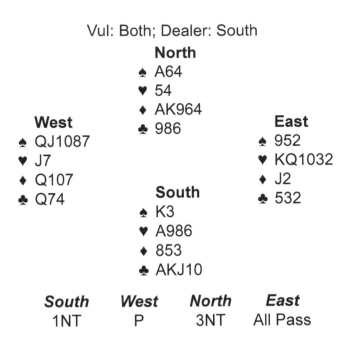

Vul: Both; Dealer: South

North
- ♠ A64
- ♥ 54
- ♦ AK964
- ♣ 986

West
- ♠ QJ1087
- ♥ J7
- ♦ Q107
- ♣ Q74

East
- ♠ 952
- ♥ KQ1032
- ♦ J2
- ♣ 532

South
- ♠ K3
- ♥ A986
- ♦ 853
- ♣ AKJ10

South	*West*	*North*	*East*
1NT	P	3NT	All Pass

Lead: ♠Q. Plan the play.

You have 7 tricks. You could take two Club finesses or you could score 4 Diamond tricks if Diamonds are 3–2. Do not just jump at the Diamonds because 3–2 Diamonds are more likely than a winning Club finesse. Ask yourself if you can combine both chances after the ♠Q lead reduces you to one Spade stopper? Setting up Dummy's 4th and 5th Diamond requires losing a Diamond trick. If you try the Club finesse first your remaining Spade stopper will be driven out and you will lose too many Spades when you lose the 3rd Diamond. Instead play the ♦A and ♦K. If both opponents follow abandon the Club finesse. Give up the third Diamond, win any return and cash your 9 tricks provided that you saved the ♠A to get to the board. If the Diamonds fail to break you stop playing Diamonds after the second Diamond and try the Club finesse. If it wins you are almost home, but look at the Clubs carefully. If you carelessly played the ♠A at trick 1 you have no way back to run the second Club finesse. Your play to trick 1 is crucial no matter how Diamonds and Clubs divide. Do not get so focused on your improving "combining" skills that you play carelessly to an early trick. Often a good combining strategy requires careful attention to the transportation between the hands.

Exercise 61

Vul: N/S; Dealer: North

North
- ♠ AK107
- ♥ Q1096
- ♦ KQ84
- ♣ 6

South
- ♠ J943
- ♥ A83
- ♦ J102
- ♣ KQ2

North	East	South	West
1♦	1NT[1]	X[2]	P
P	XX[3]	P	2♣
3♣[4]	P	3♠	P
4♠	All Pass		

1. 15–18 HCP, Diamonds stopped.
2. Penalty Double.
3. Pick a suit.
4. Extras; Pick a suit or No Trump with a Club stopper

Lead: ♣10 taken by the Ace. ♣4 returned. Plan the play.

Vul: N/S; Dealer: North

North
- ♠ AK107
- ♥ Q1096
- ♦ KQ84
- ♣ 6

West
- ♠ 852
- ♥ 42
- ♦ 653
- ♣ 109853

East
- ♠ Q6
- ♥ KJ75
- ♦ A97
- ♣ AJ74

South
- ♠ J943
- ♥ A83
- ♦ J102
- ♣ KQ2

North	East	South	West
1♦	1NT¹	X²	P
P	XX³	P	2♣
3♣⁴	P	3♠	P
4♠	All Pass		

1. 15–18 HCP, Diamonds stopped.
2. Penalty Double.
3. Pick a suit.
4. Extras; Pick a suit or No Trump with a Club stopper

Lead: ♣10 taken by the Ace. ♣4 returned. Plan the play.

You have losers in Hearts, Diamonds and Clubs so you must not lose a Spade. "Eight Ever, Nine Never" says to take the Spade finesse, twice if necessary. Have you counted your combined High Card Points? You have 25 and this deck probably has 40. East over-called 1NT (15 – 18) so how many HCP do you think that West has? Finessing West cannot win but do not give up. You know from the bidding that East has at least two Spades. Maybe East has *exactly* two Spades. It is not a good chance but it is far better than the Spade finesse that has no chance at all. The same logic locates all of the Heart honors. Lead the ♥Q, forcing East to cover, thereby losing only one Heart. Count the Opponents' HCP on *every* hand! This information combined with what you learn from the bidding and early card play will often locate key cards.

Exercise 62

Vul: None; Dealer: South

North
- ♠ QJ1094
- ♥ 98432
- ♦ 5
- ♣ 76

South
- ♠ AK732
- ♥ —
- ♦ KQ42
- ♣ 10854

South	*West*	*North*	*East*
1♠	X	4♠	All Pass

Lead: ♣K. East encourages with the ♣9. West continues with the ♣J, overtaken by East's ♣A. East returns a low Club which you ruff. Plan the play.

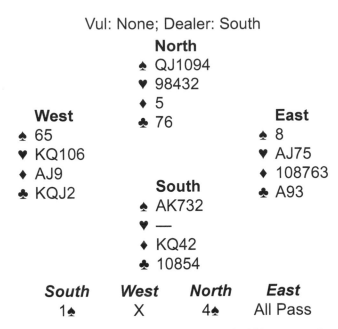

Vul: None; Dealer: South

North
♠ QJ1094
♥ 98432
♦ 5
♣ 76

West
♠ 65
♥ KQ106
♦ AJ9
♣ KQJ2

East
♠ 8
♥ AJ75
♦ 108763
♣ A93

South
♠ AK732
♥ —
♦ KQ42
♣ 10854

South	West	North	East
1♠	X	4♠	All Pass

Lead: ♣K. East encourages with the ♣9. West continues with the ♣J, overtaken by East's ♣A. East returns a low Club which you ruff. Plan the play.

Do not lead trump! This is a cross ruff hand! Lead the ♦5 to drive out the Ace. If West does not return a trump after winning the ♦A you have a high cross ruff after winning the second Diamond. You are going to make your contract.

Note that leading up to the ♦KQ will allow you to make the contract if East has the ♦A, not an impossibility on the bidding. Even if East leads a trump after winning the ♦A you will score eight trump tricks along with the two Diamonds. Lots of trump plus shortness in both hands are the ingredients of a crossruff. You must count winners, not just losers. If you have outside winners, cash them before starting the cross ruff. Otherwise, those winners will be ruffed by the Opponents at the end of the hand.

While this is a book on Declarer play this hand shows an important principle of defense. When defending against a crossruff it is almost always right to lead trump at every opportunity including the opening lead. Doing so minimizes Declarer's opportunity to play one trump per trick. The result is more tricks for the defense. If West leads the ♠6 at trick 2 and then leads another trump after winning the ♦A, South can no longer win 10 tricks.

Exercise 63

Vul: N/S; Dealer: North

North
- ♠ 73
- ♥ KQ105
- ♦ A763
- ♣ K63

South
- ♠ 964
- ♥ AJ43
- ♦ K9
- ♣ A875

North	East	South	West
1♦	P	1♥	P
2♥	P	4♥	All Pass

Lead: ♠A from AK followed by the ♠K and the ♠2 to East's ♠Q which you ruff with the ♥5. Plan the play.

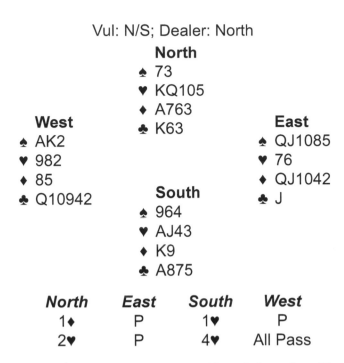

Vul: N/S; Dealer: North

North
♠ 73
♥ KQ105
♦ A763
♣ K63

West
♠ AK2
♥ 982
♦ 85
♣ Q10942

East
♠ QJ1085
♥ 76
♦ QJ1042
♣ J

South
♠ 964
♥ AJ43
♦ K9
♣ A875

North	East	South	West
1♦	P	1♥	P
2♥	P	4♥	All Pass

Lead: ♣A from AK followed by the ♠K and the ♠2 to East's ♠Q which you ruff with the ♥5. Plan the play.

Unless the Clubs are 3–3 drawing trump leaves you with only 9 tricks. With high trumps a better plan is to ruff 2 Diamonds in Declarer's hand while winning 4 trumps in Dummy plus the 2 Ace–King combinations. The chance of an Opponent having a singleton or void in Diamonds is very small. The chance of an Opponent having a singleton or void in Clubs is also low. So the chance of being able to cash your minor suit winners without them being trumped is far better than Clubs being 3–3. Give yourself a better chance by drawing 2 rounds of trump with the ♥K and ♥Q reserving the ♥A and ♥J in Declarer's hand. If the Diamonds or Clubs split badly, hopefully the person with shortness will have started with 1 or 2 trump. Cash the ♦K and ♦A and ruff a Diamond with the ♥J. Then lead low to the ♣K and ruff Dummy's last Diamond with the ♥A. Dummy now holds the ♥10 and ♣63. Your hand has ♣A87. Play the ♣A and Dummy's ♥10 is trick 10. You win 6 trumps, 2 Diamonds and 2 Clubs. This layout shows the importance of drawing two rounds of trump before playing the minors. Drawing only some of the trump is sometimes prudent.

Exercise 64

Vul: N/S; Dealer: South
Scoring: Matchpoints

North
♠ 84
♥ AQ6
♦ QJ74
♣ Q1093

South
♠ K92
♥ 98
♦ AK86
♣ AK72

South	West	North	East
1NT	P	3NT	All Pass

Lead: ♥5. Plan the play.

Vul: N/S; Dealer: South; Scoring: Matchpoints

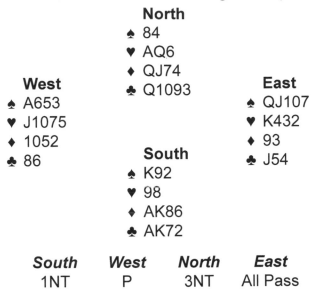

North
- ♠ 84
- ♥ AQ6
- ♦ QJ74
- ♣ Q1093

West
- ♠ A653
- ♥ J1075
- ♦ 1052
- ♣ 86

East
- ♠ QJ107
- ♥ K432
- ♦ 93
- ♣ J54

South
- ♠ K92
- ♥ 98
- ♦ AK86
- ♣ AK72

South	*West*	*North*	*East*
1NT	P	3NT	All Pass

Lead: ♥5. Plan the play.

It looks like you have 9 tricks and perhaps 10: the ♥A, 4 Clubs, 4 Diamonds plus the ♥Q if West led from the ♥K. Making 9 tricks will not count for much at matchpoints if most pairs are making 10. Many good players will use the Rule of Eleven to deduce that East has only one card higher than the ♥5, making it 2 chances in 3 that the ♥K lies with West. A free overtrick at matchpoints: what else could a bridge player want? They play the Queen at trick one and go down on this layout when East switches to the ♠Q. Expert players will see that if West holds the ♥K at trick 1 it will still be there after South plays the ♥A and 8 minor suit tricks. South should play the ♥A followed by 3 rounds of Diamonds, preserving the ♦K as an entry to hand. Playing Diamonds first might yield a clue as to who might hold long Clubs if they are not 3–2. South should then play the Clubs and the last Diamond. Only then should South lead up to the ♥Q. If West holds the ♥K, South is guaranteed 10 tricks. If not, the defense will likely take the last 4 tricks but the contract has already been made. The risk of playing the ♥Q at trick 1 is unnecessary. If you can postpone the finesse until after your contract is secure, do so, whether playing matchpoints or IMPs.

Exercise 65

Vul: N/S; Dealer: East

North
- ♠ K10653
- ♥ 7
- ♦ KQ1083
- ♣ Q7

South
- ♠ AQJ
- ♥ A952
- ♦ J74
- ♣ A106

East	South	West	North
P	1NT	P	2♥[1]
P	2♠	P	3♦[2]
P	3♠[3]	P	4♠
All Pass			

1. Transfer.
2. Game forcing; second suit.
3. Good Spade raise.

Lead: ♥K. Plan the play.

Vul: N/S; Dealer: East

North
♠ K10653
♥ 7
♦ KQ1083
♣ Q7

West
♠ 9842
♥ KQJ6
♦ —
♣ J9543

East
♠ 7
♥ 10843
♦ A9652
♣ K82

South
♠ AQJ
♥ A952
♦ J74
♣ A106

East	South	West	North
P	1NT	P	2♥¹
P	2♠	P	3♦²
P	3♠³	P	4♠
All Pass			

1. *Transfer.*
2. *Game forcing; second suit.*
3. *Good Spade raise.*

Lead: ♥K. Plan the play.

Does it seem like a good idea to try to ruff some Hearts through a Dummy Reversal? We hope not. After driving out the ♦A you have a running Diamond suit. Your solid trump suit together with 4 Diamond tricks and a trick in each black suit will bring you to 11 tricks. Why risk the bad things that can happen in a Dummy Reversal if the suits break badly? Notice that a running suit in either hand usually makes a Dummy Reversal unwise. There is one situation to be careful of. With 8 Diamonds and 4 of the top 5 you should be able to bring the suit home with only 1 loser. How do you protect yourself against the loss of a second trick if there is a 5–0 split in either direction? The solution is to play one of the honors from the long suit first. This will permit a finesse in either direction should a 5–0 split be revealed. Do not make the mistake of playing the ♦J on the first Diamond lead because that would eliminate a finesse through East.

A Declarer's Workbook

Exercise 66

Vul: Both; Dealer: East
Matchpoints

North
♠ 64
♥ A753
♦ J954
♣ A43

South
♠ A973
♥ J106
♦ AK1063
♣ 7

East	South	West	North
P	1♦	P	1♥
P	1♠	P	3♦
All Pass			

Lead: ♣10. Plan the play.

Vul: Both; Dealer: East; Matchpoints

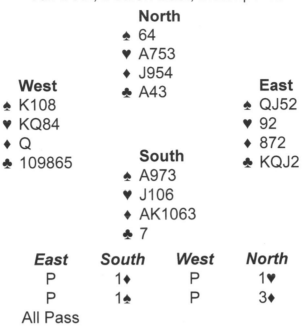

North
♠ 64
♥ A753
♦ J954
♣ A43

West
♠ K108
♥ KQ84
♦ Q
♣ 109865

East
♠ QJ52
♥ 92
♦ 872
♣ KQJ2

South
♠ A973
♥ J106
♦ AK1063
♣ 7

East	South	West	North
P	1♦	P	1♥
P	1♠	P	3♦
All Pass			

Lead: ♣10. Plan the play.

This is matchpoints so overtricks matter. If Diamonds are 2–2 you win 5 Diamonds and three Aces for eight tricks but a 3–1 split is more likely. If you fail to pick up the ♦Q you need another trick. How about a Club ruff? Remember that ruffing in the long hand does not create a trick but ruffing in the short hand does. Win the ♣A, duck a Spade and win the Ace of Spades after regaining the lead. Now you can ruff 1 or 2 Spades in Dummy – the hand with shorter trump. That creates tricks! When you regain the lead after ducking the Spade you can afford to play two rounds of Diamonds – maybe they will be 2–2. As the cards lie the ♦Q falls under the Ace. Stop playing trump until you have ruffed your two low Spades. Finish drawing trump and concede two Heart tricks. Making 4♦ is a tie for top. Making only 9 tricks is below average. The key to the hand is to recognize that a good score requires two Spade ruffs, not just one. When good fortune allows the ♦Q to fall, recognize that you can ruff two Spades and still draw trump without a loser. Always be on the lookout for ruffs in the short hand. Overtricks at matchpoints are golden!

A Declarer's Workbook

Exercise 67

Vul: Both; Dealer: South

North
- ♠ J7
- ♥ 962
- ♦ AJ64
- ♣ A1043

South
- ♠ A32
- ♥ K7
- ♦ KQ53
- ♣ QJ65

South	*West*	*North*	*East*
1NT	P	3NT	All Pass

Lead: ♠4. East covers with the ♠K. Plan the play.

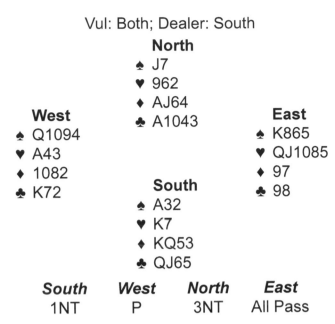

Vul: Both; Dealer: South

North
- ♠ J7
- ♥ 962
- ♦ AJ64
- ♣ A1043

West
- ♠ Q1094
- ♥ A43
- ♦ 1082
- ♣ K72

East
- ♠ K865
- ♥ QJ1085
- ♦ 97
- ♣ 98

South
- ♠ A32
- ♥ K7
- ♦ KQ53
- ♣ QJ65

South	West	North	East
1NT	P	3NT	All Pass

Lead: ♠4. East covers with the ♠K. Plan the play.

You have 6 tricks. You can get 3 more from Clubs if the finesse works. Even if it fails you can fall back on the ♥A being onside. Could West be trying to set up a 5 card Spade suit? If so, ducking twice would run East out of Spades. If you believe this hogwash you have fallen into the "when in doubt, duck" trap. If you duck trick 1 your contract could fail. East could lead the ♥Q and you will be faced with a big problem. If you look carefully at your hand you will see the ♠3 and ♠2. The ♠4 is West's lowest. You need to ask East what the Opponents' lead agreement is. If they are leading fourth best that would indicate that West very likely has 4 Spades, though West could certainly be leading low from 3, leaving East, not West, with 5. Since the unavoidable Club finesse is going into East, ducking does you no good. More importantly, whenever you are faced with a duck-no duck decision ask yourself what the person winning the trick might switch to. In this case you should fear a Heart shift. You could be set before you can try the Club finesse. The correct choice is to play the ♠J in case West led from the ♠KQ. If the ♠J is covered win the ♠A and immediately take the Club finesse by leading low to the ♣10 in case the ♣K is singleton with West. If the ♣10 wins come back to your hand and lead the ♣Q. If the Clubs are 3–2 you make your contract. If the ♣10 loses you need the ♥A to be onside. Play accordingly. Ducking is a useful play in many hands but always consider if a shift of suits might not be a greater danger. Such is the case here.

Exercise 68

Vul: Both; Dealer: North

North
- ♠ K742
- ♥ Q954
- ♦ K532
- ♣ A

South
- ♠ J863
- ♥ AK7
- ♦ AQ87
- ♣ 84

North	East	South	West
1♦	P	1♠	P
2♠	P	4♠	All Pass

Lead: ♣K. Plan the play.

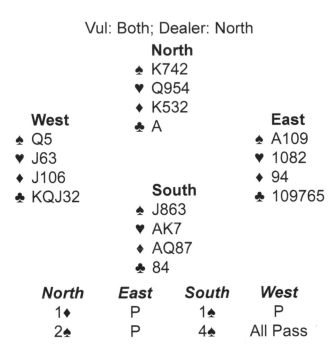

Vul: Both; Dealer: North

North
♠ K742
♥ Q954
♦ K532
♣ A

West
♠ Q5
♥ J63
♦ J106
♣ KQJ32

East
♠ A109
♥ 1082
♦ 94
♣ 109765

South
♠ J863
♥ AK7
♦ AQ87
♣ 84

North	East	South	West
1♦	P	1♠	P
2♣	P	4♠	All Pass

Lead: ♣K. Plan the play.

Your side suits are solid so you can probably afford 3 trump losers. Kxx(x) facing Jxx(x) is a suit you want the Opponents to lead but that is not going to happen. You cannot afford to defer drawing trump. If you do, one or more of your side suit tricks will get ruffed with a small trump and then you are likely to go down. You must draw trump and you must start as soon as you win the ♣A. The correct way to play this combination is to come to your hand with the ♥A to lead a trump to the ♠7 unless West plays a higher card. If West plays the ♠Q, ♠10 or ♠9 play the ♠K from Dummy. If West plays the ♠5 you must insert the ♠7 to force out an honor. Do not play the ♠K. This approach will expose a singleton ♠A or ♠Q or attempt to promote Declarer's ♠J and ♠8. If the ♠7 loses to the ♠9 or ♠10 you should lead up to the ♠K after regaining the lead. You hold your trump losers to 3 whenever trump are 3–2 or they are 4–1 with either the ♠A or ♠Q onside or singleton or the defense errs. There is a good chance of one of these things happening so do not be afraid. You go down only when trump are 5–0 or 4–1 with both the ♠A and ♠Q offside and not singleton. Once you have drawn trump, turn your attention to the side suits. You can score 7 tricks in Diamonds and Hearts if Diamonds are 3–2 or Hearts are 3–3. Keep both possibilities in mind.

A Declarer's Workbook

Exercise 69

Vul: E/W; Dealer: East

North
- ♠ K9765
- ♥ J96
- ♦ 542
- ♣ 63

South
- ♠ A10843
- ♥ Q52
- ♦ AK7
- ♣ 95

East	South	West	North
P	1♠	X	3♠¹
All Pass			

1. Preemptive.

Lead: ♦Q. Plan the play.

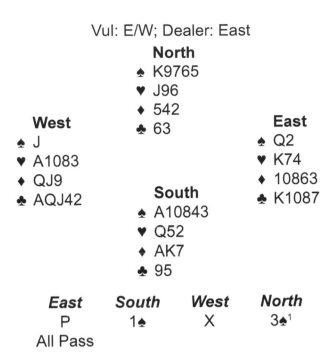

Vul: E/W; Dealer: East

North
♠ K9765
♥ J96
♦ 542
♣ 63

West
♠ J
♥ A1083
♦ QJ9
♣ AQJ42

East
♠ Q2
♥ K74
♦ 10863
♣ K1087

South
♠ A10843
♥ Q52
♦ AK7
♣ 95

East	South	West	North
P	1♠	X	3♠[1]
All Pass			

1. Preemptive.

Lead: ♦Q. Plan the play.

North's preemptive 3♠ has kept the Opponents out of a good Club partial. You have to lose a Diamond and 2 Clubs. Can you hold the Heart losers to 2 to get a score of –50? Jxx opposite Qxx is one of those suits you need the Opponents to lead because if you lead it you are a likely to lose three tricks. If only your Clubs and Diamonds weren't square this would be easy. But wait!! Square suits and extra trump can sometimes be turned into a strip and end play. Win the ♦A, draw trump and play your ♦K and a low Diamond. The Opponents can win two Club tricks but then whoever is on lead has no safe exit. The difference between –50 or –100 is important. At Matchpoints it will likely be the difference between a good board and an excellent one. At IMPs it will save you 2 IMPs, and that could turn a 1 point loss into a 1 point win. Even if you are going down it almost always pays to save a trick.

A Declarer's Workbook

Exercise 70

Vul: None; Dealer: East

North
- ♠ 7
- ♥ A9542
- ♦ K1095
- ♣ A76

South
- ♠ AQJ106
- ♥ KQ73
- ♦ 86
- ♣ 94

East	South	West	North
P	1♠	P	1NT[1]
P	2♥	P	4♥

All Pass

1. One round force.

Lead: ♣K. East plays the ♣8, standard count. Plan the play.

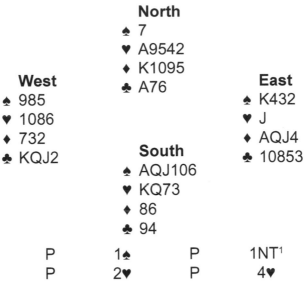

North
- ♠ 7
- ♥ A9542
- ♦ K1095
- ♣ A76

West
- ♠ 985
- ♥ 1086
- ♦ 732
- ♣ KQJ2

East
- ♠ K432
- ♥ J
- ♦ AQJ4
- ♣ 10853

South
- ♠ AQJ106
- ♥ KQ73
- ♦ 86
- ♣ 94

P	1♠	P	1NT¹
P	2♥	P	4♥

All Pass

1. One round force.

Lead: ♣K. East plays the ♣8, standard count. Plan the play.

Even if drawing trump takes 3 rounds you could finesse East once in Spades and then try to ruff out the ♠K. Another approach is to lead up to the ♠A and use a ruffing finesse against West. Which is best? Finessing into West could be a disaster if the finesse loses. West could lead a Diamond. The ruffing finesse is safe because if it loses, East will not be able to attack Diamonds. Hopefully you have not yet played to trick 1. Since the Spade finesse is going into East you should think about what East will do if the finesse loses and East has the ♦A. East will need a Diamond lead from West. If you win the first Club trick East will know to lead to West's ♣Q. West will have no trouble finding a Diamond shift at this point and down you go. You can sever this communication by ducking the first Club. To counter this strategy West has to perceive *at trick 2* that an immediate Diamond shift is needed. It is much harder for West to find this shift at trick 2 then it will be at trick 5 or 6. Think through the entire hand before playing to trick 1. If the ♠K and the ♦A rest with East you always go down on perfect defense. Ducking at trick 1 makes that harder to achieve.

A Declarer's Workbook

Exercise 71

Vul: Both; Dealer: West

North
- ♠ KQ64
- ♥ A1085
- ♦ K75
- ♣ J3

South
- ♠ J832
- ♥ KJ62
- ♦ A64
- ♣ A7

West	North	East	South
P	1♦	P	1♥
P	2♥	P	4♥
All Pass			

Lead: ♣K. Plan the play.

Vul: Both; Dealer: West

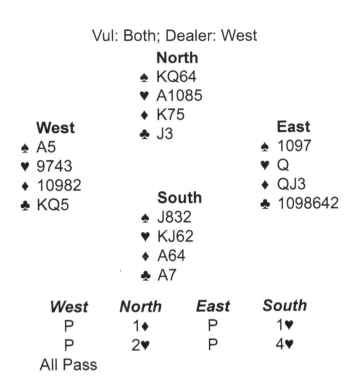

North
- ♠ KQ64
- ♥ A1085
- ♦ K75
- ♣ J3

West
- ♠ A5
- ♥ 9743
- ♦ 10982
- ♣ KQ5

East
- ♠ 1097
- ♥ Q
- ♦ QJ3
- ♣ 1098642

South
- ♠ J832
- ♥ KJ62
- ♦ A64
- ♣ A7

West	North	East	South
P	1♦	P	1♥
P	2♥	P	4♥
All Pass			

Lead: ♣K. Plan the play.

You have a loser in each side suit. 3NT would have been easier but you have to bring Hearts home without a loser. You have no information about the Opponents' hands so 8 Ever 9 Never applies. Take a finesse to find the ♥Q – a 50/50 guess. If Hearts are 3–2 guessing the Queen correctly will suffice. If Hearts are 4–1 you might have to finesse for the ♥9 because West will cover the ♥J when holding the ♥Q9xx. Winning 4 Heart tricks will require a finesse through the ♥9. The same play cannot be made through East so you need to plan for the only 4–1 break you can handle by running the Heart finesses through West. Win the ♣A, cross to the ♦K and lead up to the ♥K. Lo and behold, the ♥Q falls. Now what? You cannot afford to draw trump before driving out the ♠A because Clubs are wide open. First drive out the ♠A. If the defense plays Clubs you ruff the third round in hand, finish drawing trump and claim 10 tricks. Playing the ♥K first to drop a stiff ♥Q is right because you hold the ♥J and ♥10. If you did not hold the ♥10 then you would not have 4 top trump if the ♥Q fell singleton and Hearts were 4–1. Your strategy would have to be different. Can you guess what kind of problem might lie ahead?

Exercise 72

Vul: N/S; Dealer: East

North
- ♠ AKJ
- ♥ 1096
- ♦ KJ4
- ♣ AJ98

South
- ♠ Q7643
- ♥ AJ2
- ♦ AQ53
- ♣ 6

East	South	West	North
P	1♠	P	2♣[1]
P	2♦	P	2♠[2]
P	4♣[3]	P	4♦[4]
P	4NT[5]	P	5♦[6]
P	6♠	All Pass	

1. Game forcing.
2. Spade support with slam interest.
3. Club shortness.
4. Diamond control.
5. RKC 1430
6. Zero or 3 Key Cards.

Lead: ♣K. Plan the play.

Vul: N/S; Dealer: East

North
- ♠ AKJ
- ♥ 1096
- ♦ KJ4
- ♣ AJ98

West
- ♠ 852
- ♥ KQ5
- ♦ 10872
- ♣ KQ7

East
- ♠ 109
- ♥ 8743
- ♦ 96
- ♣ 105432

South
- ♠ Q7643
- ♥ AJ2
- ♦ AQ53
- ♣ 6

East	South	West	North
P	1♠	P	2♣¹
P	2♦	P	2♠²
P	4♣³	P	4♦⁴
P	4NT⁵	P	5♦⁶
P	6♠	All Pass	

1. Game forcing.
2. Spade support with slam interest.
3. Club shortness.
4. Diamond control.
5. RKC 1430
6. Zero or 3 Key Cards.

Lead: ♣K. Plan the play.

At first glance this looks like a simple hand. If East has a Heart honor you can finesse East twice. If West has both honors, you go down. Good players will see one other small chance that is worth testing because it risks nothing. If trumps are 3–2 you will be able to ruff two Clubs. Maybe West's ♣Q (promised by the opening lead) will fall. Win the opening lead, ruff a Club and then draw trumps, ending in Dummy if trumps are 3–2. Lead the ♥10. If East covers, win the trick, concede a Heart trick and claim. If East does not cover allow West to win. The best return is a Diamond. Win in dummy and ruff a Club. If the ♣Q falls your ♣J is your twelfth trick and you can get to it with a Diamond. If the ♣Q does not fall, return to Dummy with a Diamond and repeat the Heart finesse. If East has the other Heart honor you make your slam. If not, take comfort in the fact that you gave yourself every chance.

A Declarer's Workbook

Exercise 73

Vul: None; Dealer: South

North
- ♠ Q43
- ♥ 96
- ♦ 864
- ♣ AKQ75

South
- ♠ AK65
- ♥ K43
- ♦ A107
- ♣ J42

South	West	North	East
1NT	P	3NT	All Pass

Lead: ♦5. East plays the ♦Q. Plan the play.

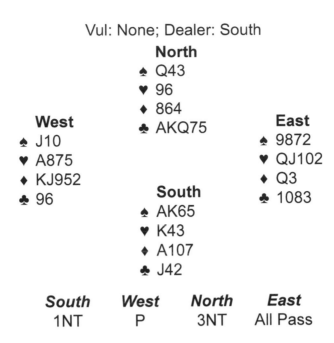

Vul: None; Dealer: South

North
♠ Q43
♥ 96
♦ 864
♣ AKQ75

West
♠ J10
♥ A875
♦ KJ952
♣ 96

East
♠ 9872
♥ QJ102
♦ Q3
♣ 1083

South
♠ AK65
♥ K43
♦ A107
♣ J42

South	West	North	East
1NT	P	3NT	All Pass

Lead: ♦5. East plays the ♦Q. Plan the play.

Since you have 6 Diamonds between the two hands this looks like one of those hands where you duck 1 Diamond trick and then capture the second trick in order to run East out of Diamonds if they are 5–2. If you do that without counting your tricks and looking where the real danger lies you could be very embarrassed. There is no law requiring East to return partner's lead. What will happen if East switches to the ♥Q? What is worse, did you count your tricks? Unless Clubs are 5–0 you have 5 Clubs, 1 Diamond and 3 Spades. The lesson here is that you must not develop the bad habit of just ducking automatically. Often ducking for a round or two is right but each hand is unique. Plan the entire hand, considering all of your options. If ducking is right, do it. But before doing so ask yourself if there is a switch available that could prove more dangerous than the suit that was led. Certainly that is the case on this hand.

A Declarer's Workbook

Exercise 74

Vul: Both; Dealer: South

North
- ♠ K1072
- ♥ KJ5
- ♦ K742
- ♣ 75

South
- ♠ AJ865
- ♥ Q7
- ♦ AJ65
- ♣ K9

South	West	North	East
1♠	P	3♠¹	P
4♠	All Pass		

1. Four card limit raise.

Lead: ♦10. Plan the play.

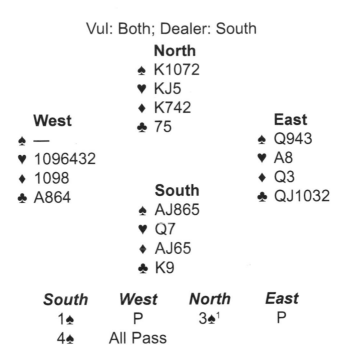

Vul: Both; Dealer: South

North
♠ K1072
♥ KJ5
♦ K742
♣ 75

West
♠ —
♥ 1096432
♦ 1098
♣ A864

East
♠ Q943
♥ A8
♦ Q3
♣ QJ1032

South
♠ AJ865
♥ Q7
♦ AJ65
♣ K9

South	West	North	East
1♠	P	3♠[1]	P
4♠	All Pass		

1. Four card limit raise.

Lead: ♦10. Plan the play.

The threat is West holding the ♣A and East leading Clubs. We can discard a Club on Dummy's third Heart but we must lose to the ♥A first. If East has the ♥A we could lose a Heart and 2 Clubs regardless of what happens in trump. Can you get a count on the hand by playing Hearts before drawing trump? Our worst case is the ♥A with East and the ♣A with West so HCP will not help. Since only one Heart trick and two Club tricks are involved that will not tell us much. We also need to think about a 4–0 trump split. We have almost no information about the Opponents' cards so Eight Ever, Nine Ever applies. Since we have nine Spades we are going to play to drop the Queen. Be careful when you play those two tricks! We eliminate one chance for East to get the lead by winning the opening lead in hand (taking advantage of the free Diamond finesse) and leading low to the ♠K. If East has all of the Spades we will know when West discards and we can play Spades to avoid a loser because of our good spot cards.

Exercise 75

Vul: Both; Dealer: East

North
- ♠ A973
- ♥ Q1093
- ♦ K73
- ♣ K8

South
- ♠ 2
- ♥ AKJ42
- ♦ A52
- ♣ A732

East	South	West	North
P	1♥	P	2NT[1]
P	3♠[2]	P	4♣[3]
P	4NT[4]	P	5♦[5]
P	6♥	All Pass	

1. Game forcing with four trump.
2. Spade shortness.
3. Club control.
4. RKC.
5. 1 or 4 Key Cards.

Lead: ♦Q. Plan the play.

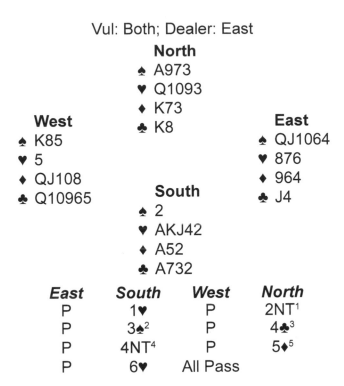

Vul: Both; Dealer: East

North
♠ A973
♥ Q1093
♦ K73
♣ K8

West
♠ K85
♥ 5
♦ QJ108
♣ Q10965

East
♠ QJ1064
♥ 876
♦ 964
♣ J4

South
♠ 2
♥ AKJ42
♦ A52
♣ A732

East	South	West	North
P	1♥	P	2NT¹
P	3♠²	P	4♣³
P	4NT⁴	P	5♦⁵
P	6♥	All Pass	

1. *Game forcing with four trump.*
2. *Spade shortness.*
3. *Club control.*
4. *RKC.*
5. *1 or 4 Key Cards.*

Lead: ♦Q. Plan the play.

If trump are 2–2 this is easy. With a sure Diamond loser what will you do if trump are 3–1 or 4–0? If you draw all of the trump you will be left with 1 or 2 Club losers. Notice the high trump in Dummy and the Spade shortness in hand. You have the entries for a Dummy Reversal if you plan on it from trick 1 by winning the ♦A (saving the ♦K as an entry to ruff Spades). If you play the ♥AK to test trump you will not have a way back to Dummy to finish drawing trump after ruffing three Spades. Trump will be 3–1 or 4–0 more often than 2–2 so plan on a bad split. Win the ♦A, lead to the ♠A and ruff a Spade low. Use the ♣K and ♦K to reenter Dummy to ruff two more Spades ruffing high. Win one round of trump with your remaining high trump and use the carefully preserved ♥4 to get to Dummy to draw the remaining trump, pitching low Clubs. Lead to your ♣A and concede a Diamond. This approach works for any trump split as long all defenders with trump hold at least two Diamonds and one Club – a far better chance than 2–2 Hearts.

A Declarer's Workbook

Exercise 76

Vul: N/S; Dealer: South
Scoring: IMPs

North
♠ 84
♥ AQ6
♦ QJ74
♣ Q1093

South
♠ K92
♥ 98
♦ AK86
♣ AK72

South	West	North	East
1NT	P	3NT	All Pass

Lead: ♥5. Plan the play.

Vul: N/S; Dealer: South; Scoring: IMPs

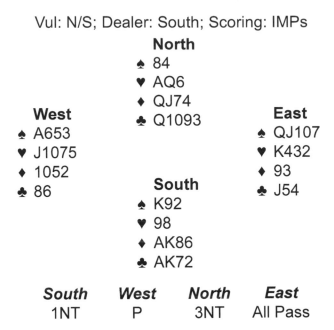

North
- ♠ 84
- ♥ AQ6
- ♦ QJ74
- ♣ Q1093

West
- ♠ A653
- ♥ J1075
- ♦ 1052
- ♣ 86

East
- ♠ QJ107
- ♥ K432
- ♦ 93
- ♣ J54

South
- ♠ K92
- ♥ 98
- ♦ AK86
- ♣ AK72

South	*West*	*North*	*East*
1NT	P	3NT	All Pass

Lead: ♥5. Plan the play.

We have seen these North/South cards before but at matchpoints. Experienced declarers will recognize that playing the ♥Q at trick one puts the game contract in jeopardy. They will focus first on guaranteeing +600. Only then will they search for an overtrick. They can guarantee nine tricks by taking the ♥A and finding the ♣J, postponing leading to the ♥Q. After winning the ♥A they will play Diamonds before Clubs to get a read on the distribution in case a finesse is needed for the Clubs. On this layout that problem does not exist. South should arrange to take the ninth trick in hand and then lead up to the ♥Q. If West holds the ♥K South will get a tenth trick, either in Spades or Hearts. If East holds the ♥K then South will likely get a Spade lead through the ♠K and take no more tricks. The Heart finesse at trick one is a poor play, whether at IMPs or matchpoints. It gains nothing while putting the contract in jeopardy. Defenders sometimes underlead a King particularly on opening lead at No Trump. Before taking the Heart finesse at trick 1, consider postponing it. Perhaps you can ensure your contract and lead up to the Queen later. That is the correct play on these North/South cards whether at matchpoints or at IMPs.

Exercise 77

Vul: N/S; Dealer: South

North
- ♠ K87
- ♥ 6
- ♦ KQ532
- ♣ AJ76

South
- ♠ AQ1064
- ♥ K107
- ♦ A874
- ♣ 4

South	West	North	East
1♠	P	2♦¹	P
3♦	P	3♠²	P
4♦³	P	4NT⁴	P
5♠⁵	P	6♠	All Pass

1. Game force.
2. 3 card Spade support with slam interest.
3. Diamond control.
4. RKC 1430
5. 2 Key Cards plus the ♠Q.

Lead: ♠2. Plan the play.

Vul: N/S; Dealer: South

North
- ♠ K87
- ♥ 6
- ♦ KQ532
- ♣ AJ76

West
- ♠ 92
- ♥ A9842
- ♦ J6
- ♣ Q953

East
- ♠ J53
- ♥ QJ53
- ♦ 109
- ♣ K1082

South
- ♠ AQ1064
- ♥ K107
- ♦ A874
- ♣ 4

South	West	North	East
1♠	P	2♦¹	P
3♦	P	3♠²	P
4♦³	P	4NT⁴	P
5♠⁵	P	6♠	All Pass

1. *Game force.*
2. *3 card Spade support with slam interest.*
3. *Diamond control.*
4. *RKC 1430*
5. *2 Key Cards plus the ♠Q.*

Lead: ♠2. Plan the play.

A nice auction has led to a good slam. Particularly in a slam Declarer should count winners, not just losers. With the trump lead you can duck on the board and win as cheaply as possible, thereby protecting yourself from a 4–1 trump split. If you draw trump immediately you will win 5 Spades, 5 Diamonds (assuming a reasonable split) and 1 Club. That leaves you a trick short. One approach is to lead up to the ♥K. If you make that play after trump has been drawn you will have lost a great opportunity to protect your contract. Win the first trick in hand, cross to the ♣A and lead up to the ♥K. If the ♥K wins, ruff a Heart immediately, play the ♠K, ruff a Club, finish drawing trump and claim with an overtrick. If East takes the ♥A or if the ♥K loses to West, win any return and get to your hand to ruff a Heart. Draw trump and claim. The key play is not drawing trump before leading up to the ♥K. You must prepare for losing the ♥K to West's Ace. Plan to ruff a Heart in Dummy before drawing trump.

A Declarer's Workbook

Exercise 78

Vul: Both; Dealer: South
Scoring: Matchpoints

North
- ♠ K1074
- ♥ 65
- ♦ AQJ93
- ♣ 106

South
- ♠ AJ9
- ♥ A973
- ♦ 106
- ♣ AK95

South	West	North	East
1NT	P	2♣	P
2♥	P	3NT	All Pass

Lead: ♥K. East plays the ♥8 (standard signals). Plan the play.

Vul: Both; Dealer: South; Scoring: Matchpoints

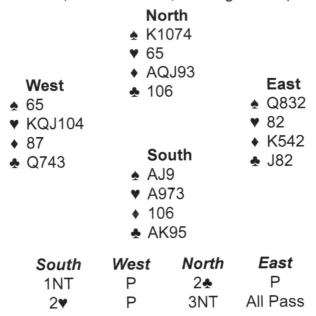

	North	
	♠ K1074	
	♥ 65	
	♦ AQJ93	
	♣ 106	

West		East
♠ 65		♠ Q832
♥ KQJ104		♥ 82
♦ 87		♦ K542
♣ Q743		♣ J82

	South	
	♠ AJ9	
	♥ A973	
	♦ 106	
	♣ AK95	

South	*West*	*North*	*East*
1NT	P	2♣	P
2♥	P	3NT	All Pass

Lead: ♥K. East plays the ♥8 (standard signals). Plan the play.

What does the ♥8 tell you? It could be a singleton or the start of a high/low to show a doubleton. It could also be an encouraging signal if East holds the ♥J. The standard lead at No Trump from KQ10x is the Q but not all players remember that. It must be best to duck the first trick and see what is played next. West might give away the show by leading the bottom of the sequence but a good player will continue with the ♥Q. When East follows with the ♥2 what do you think? While other holdings are possible, by far the most likely holding for East is the doubleton ♥82. If that is so you should win the trick and take the Spade and Diamond finesses into East since East no longer has a way back to West's hand. But wait! Since you can afford 2 Heart losers might it not make sense to duck again, just to be sure? That way, even if both finesses lose East will surely be out of Hearts and your contract will be safe. At IMPs this might be a good safety play. Do not duck more times than necessary, particularly at Matchpoints.

A Declarer's Workbook

Exercise 79

Vul: Both; Dealer: West

North
- ♠ KQ64
- ♥ A1085
- ♦ K75
- ♣ J3

South
- ♠ J832
- ♥ KJ62
- ♦ A64
- ♣ A7

West	North	East	South
P	1♦	P	1♥
P	2♥	P	4♥
All Pass			

Lead: ♦10. Plan the play.

Vul: Both; Dealer: West

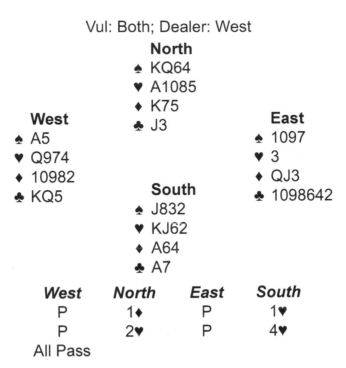

North
- ♠ KQ64
- ♥ A1085
- ♦ K75
- ♣ J3

West
- ♠ A5
- ♥ Q974
- ♦ 10982
- ♣ KQ5

East
- ♠ 1097
- ♥ 3
- ♦ QJ3
- ♣ 1098642

South
- ♠ J832
- ♥ KJ62
- ♦ A64
- ♣ A7

West	North	East	South
P	1♦	P	1♥
P	2♥	P	4♥
All Pass			

Lead: ♦10. Plan the play.

You have seen these N/S hands and this bidding sequence before. This time you get a ♦10 opening lead. Just like before, the location of the ♥Q is a 50/50 guess. If you guess wrong you go down. If Hearts are 3–2 and you guess correctly you make your contract. The ♥10 and ♥8 also allow you to make the hand if you get a 4–1 trump split with West holding the top 2 missing trump. This is an additional possibility that experts see and average players often do not. You must plan the sequence of tricks very carefully to succeed and you have to do this before you know you have a problem. Win the ♦K, not the ♦A. Preserve that entry. When you lead a low Heart to the ♥K everyone follows. When you play the ♥J West covers and East shows out. This is your lucky day!! You can make this hand while others do not as long as you are careful. You can only get back to your hand in a minor and doing so will expose that suit. You have to drive out the ♠A before you finish drawing trump. When you regain the lead after losing the ♠A, get to hand with a minor suit Ace and take the marked finesse against the ♥9. Notice that everything could fail if you win the ♦A at trick 1. Always make a thorough plan before playing to trick 1.

Exercise 80

Vul: N/S; Dealer: West

North
- ♠ A75
- ♥ KJ84
- ♦ 852
- ♣ K75

South
- ♠ K82
- ♥ AQ7
- ♦ KJ6
- ♣ A863

West	North	East	South
2♦[1]	P	P	2NT[2]
P	3♣	P	3♦
P	3NT	All Pass	

1. Preemptive.
2. 15 – 18 Balanced and Diamonds stopped.

Lead: ♠6. Plan the play.

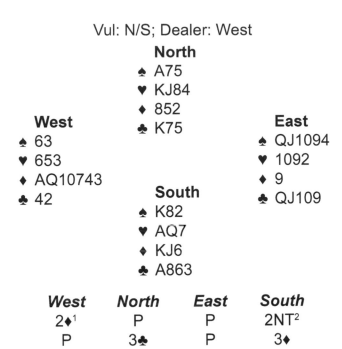

Vul: N/S; Dealer: West

North
♠ A75
♥ KJ84
♦ 852
♣ K75

West
♠ 63
♥ 653
♦ AQ10743
♣ 42

East
♠ QJ1094
♥ 1092
♦ 9
♣ QJ109

South
♠ K82
♥ AQ7
♦ KJ6
♣ A863

West	North	East	South
2♦[1]	P	P	2NT[2]
P	3♣	P	3♦
P	3NT	All Pass	

1. Preemptive.
2. 15 – 18 Balanced and Diamonds stopped.

Lead: ♠6. Plan the play.

You have eight tricks and no intermediate cards. Where can you get the ninth trick? Do you want to lead up to the KJ6 of Diamonds twice hoping that either the Ace or Queen is to your right? Since West did not lead a fourth best Diamond where do you think those honors lie? Would you lead fourth best from the ♦AQ on the auction you just heard? Clearly leading up to the ♦KJ6 is doomed. What has the bidding told you about West's hand? 2♦ promised 6 Diamonds leaving 7 other cards. If you play your eight winners what will West do? West will have to play non-Diamonds on the first seven tricks and a small Diamond on the eighth. If you win your eighth trick in dummy, for example with the fourth Heart, you can then lead a Diamond and insert either the ♦K or ♦J. West will win and have no choice but to lead a Diamond back to you, thereby establishing a Diamond winner in your hand. Not all strip and end plays involve trump. Sometimes the bidding tells you how to get the lead you need.

A Declarer's Workbook

Exercise 81

Vul: Both; Dealer: South

North
- ♠ —
- ♥ 76432
- ♦ A10976
- ♣ 876

South
- ♠ 9743
- ♥ —
- ♦ KQJ83
- ♣ AK42

South	West	North	East
1♦	2♦¹	5♦	5♠
6♦	X	All Pass	

1. 5–5 or better in the majors. < 12 HCP or > 15 HCP.

Lead: ♥A. Plan the play.

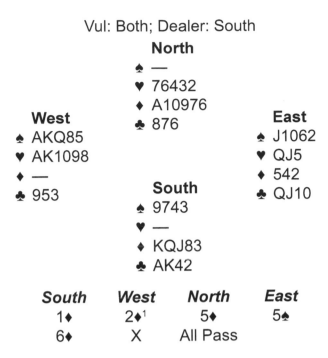

Vul: Both; Dealer: South

North
♠ —
♥ 76432
♦ A10976
♣ 876

West
♠ AKQ85
♥ AK1098
♦ —
♣ 953

East
♠ J1062
♥ QJ5
♦ 542
♣ QJ10

South
♠ 9743
♥ —
♦ KQJ83
♣ AK42

South	West	North	East
1♦	2♦[1]	5♦	5♠
6♦	X	All Pass	

1. *5–5 or better in the majors. < 12 HCP or > 15 HCP.*

Lead: ♥A. Plan the play.

After West's Michaels bid North sees the Spade void and Heart and Diamond length and visualizes a crossruff and that E/W are likely to have a Spade game or slam. The 5♦ bid makes E/W decide at the 5 level. East sees a Spade and Heart fit and the Diamond holding means West must be void. Give West a Club card and a Spade slam is likely so East bids 5♠. South sees the Club controls and figures North for a Spade void. Hence the 6♦ bid. West sees three Club losers and tosses out the double card. West smells a Spade void hence the ♥A lead. South sees a high crossruff; 5 Heart ruffs in hand and 4 Spade ruffs and another trump in dummy. Add 2 Club tricks and a doubled slam is in the bag. South ruffs the ♥A and wins the ♣A and ♣K before starting the crossruff; ruff a Spade, ruff a Heart, etc. If you do not win the Club tricks before starting the crossruff one of them might get ruffed at the end, ***When executing a high crossruff take your outside winners first.*** This prevents a defender from discarding losers and ruffing one of those winners.

Exercise 82

Vul: N/S; Dealer: East

North
- ♠ Q1042
- ♥ 3
- ♦ AQJ76
- ♣ 842

South
- ♠ AKJ853
- ♥ AK5
- ♦ 10
- ♣ K53

East	South	West	North
P	1♠	P	2NT¹
P	3♦²	P	4♥³
P	4NT⁴	P	5♣⁵
P	5♦⁶	P	5NT⁷
P	6♠	All Pass	

1. *Four card game force.*
2. *Diamond shortness.*
3. *Heart shortness.*
4. *RKC 1430.*
5. *1 or 4 Key Cards.*
6. *Queen ask.*
7. *Queen of trump but no outside King.*

Lead: ♠6. Plan the play.

Vul: N/S; Dealer: East

North
- ♠ Q1042
- ♥ 3
- ♦ AQJ76
- ♣ 842

West
- ♠ 76
- ♥ J1076
- ♦ K93
- ♣ A1096

East
- ♠ 9
- ♥ Q9842
- ♦ 8542
- ♣ QJ7

South
- ♠ AKJ853
- ♥ AK5
- ♦ 10
- ♣ K53

East	South	West	North
P	1♠	P	2NT¹
P	3♦²	P	4♥³
P	4NT⁴	P	5♣⁵
P	5♦⁶	P	5NT⁷
P	6♠	All Pass	
All Pass			

1. *Four card game force.*
2. *Diamond shortness.*
3. *Heart shortness.*
4. *RKC 1430.*

5. *1 or 4 Key Cards.*
6. *Queen ask.*
7. *Queen of trump but no outside King.*

Lead: ♠6. Plan the play.

One of Dummy's Clubs will go on your ♥K. If you draw trump, play the ♥AK and go to Dummy to lead up to the ♣K you are missing a chance in Diamonds. Diamonds will split 4–3 most of the time. If they do, one Opponent will sometimes have Kxx and you can drop the ♦K in three leads. Most importantly, you can test Diamonds without losing the lead and lead up to the ♣K if necessary. Win the opening lead in hand and play the ♥AK to pitch a Club. Then lead the ♦10 and play the ♦A. If West covers you make 7♠. If not, ruff a low Diamond high and lead a medium trump to get back to Dummy. Now lead the ♦Q. Maybe the ♦K will fall or East will err by covering. If so, the ♦J7 are good. Get to Dummy with a trump to pitch two Clubs on the Diamonds. However, if the ♦K is still hiding, use a trump to get to Dummy and lead up to the ♣K. Diamonds will sometimes set up and you can see if they do with no risk – a very nice combining play.

A Declarer's Workbook

Exercise 83

Vul: Both; Dealer: West

North
- ♠ AQ76
- ♥ 74
- ♦ AQJ105
- ♣ 82

South
- ♠ K10543
- ♥ AJ63
- ♦ 7
- ♣ A95

West	North	East	South
1♥	2♦	P	2♠
P	4♠	All Pass	

Lead: ♣K. East plays the ♣7, standard count. Plan the play.

Vul: Both; Dealer: West

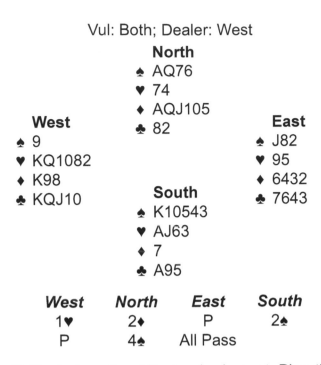

North
♠ AQ76
♥ 74
♦ AQJ105
♣ 82

West
♠ 9
♥ KQ1082
♦ K98
♣ KQJ10

East
♠ J82
♥ 95
♦ 6432
♣ 7643

South
♠ K10543
♥ AJ63
♦ 7
♣ A95

West	North	East	South
1♥	2♦	P	2♠
P	4♠	All Pass	

Lead: ♣K. East plays the ♣7, standard count. Plan the play.

You need to ruff a Heart loser in Dummy so assume Spades are no worse than 3–1. West has an opening hand but did not bid after South's 2♠ so West probably does not have 7 Hearts. That means West almost surely has 11+ HCP. This locates the ♦K. We need Heart and Club pitches so plan on running the Diamonds after drawing trump. How should Diamonds be played? Since you know where the ♦K sits you can win the ♣A and finesse the ♦Q. Ruff the ♦5 and draw trump ending in Dummy. Play the ♦A discarding a Club from hand and dropping West's ♦K. Dummy's ♦J10 are resting spots for Declarer's last Club and a Heart. Your only loser will be a Heart. With AQJ10x opposite a singleton it is often right to win the first Diamond with the ♦A and take a ruffing finesse through East but not on this hand. Notice that the bidding locates the ♦K and ♦Kxx is certainly a possibility. Taking the Diamond finesse, ruffing a Diamond and winning the ♦A after drawing trump allows you to make 12 tricks when others are making only 11.

Exercise 84

Vul: Both; Dealer: North

North
- ♠ A4
- ♥ 7532
- ♦ QJ4
- ♣ KQ73

South
- ♠ K7
- ♥ K1086
- ♦ K62
- ♣ A962

North	East	South	West
1♣	P	1♥	P
2♥	P	4♥	All Pass

Lead: ♠Q. Plan the play.

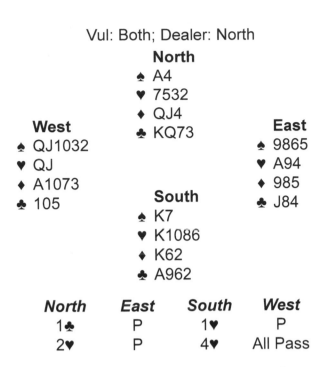

Vul: Both; Dealer: North

North
- ♠ A4
- ♥ 7532
- ♦ QJ4
- ♣ KQ73

West
- ♠ QJ1032
- ♥ QJ
- ♦ A1073
- ♣ 105

East
- ♠ 9865
- ♥ A94
- ♦ 985
- ♣ J84

South
- ♠ K7
- ♥ K1086
- ♦ K62
- ♣ A962

North	East	South	West
1♣	P	1♥	P
2♥	P	4♥	All Pass

Lead: ♠Q. Plan the play.

You have a sure Diamond loser so you must hold your trump losers to 2. You need a 3–2 trump split and either the ♥A onside or a way to force the Opponents to put a high trump on air. To give yourself the best chance, win the first trick with the ♠A and lead up to the ♥8. That is not a misprint. Play the ♥8, not the ♥10, if East plays the ♥4. (Play the ♥10 if East plays the ♥9.) Remember, you need a Heart honor to go on that ♥8 if the ♥A is offside. Regardless of the fate of the ♥8, when you regain the lead go to Dummy with a Club and lead up to the ♥10 unless East plays a higher card. On the layout shown you come out a winner. The point of this lesson is that there is a 50% chance of the ♥9 resting with East. If that is the case, West will be forced to play an honor on the ♥8. This gives you a chance to finesse East for the remaining ♥Q or ♥J by playing the ♥10. You are not a favorite to make this contract but playing the ♥8 gives you the best chance. Playing the ♥10 instead of the ♥8 when East plays the ♥4 is inferior because it will lose to the ♥Q or ♥J 75% of the time and you will not have promoted your ♥8 because it will lose to either the ♥9 or the ♥Q or ♥J, which ever remains in play.

A Declarer's Workbook

Exercise 85

Vul: Both; Dealer: South

North
- ♠ KJ72
- ♥ KJ5
- ♦ QJ42
- ♣ 75

South
- ♠ A10865
- ♥ Q73
- ♦ AK6
- ♣ K9

South	West	North	East
1♠	P	3♠[1]	P
4♠	All Pass		

1. Four card limit raise.

Lead: ♦10. Plan the play.

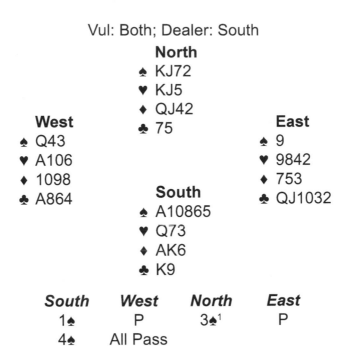

Vul: Both; Dealer: South

North
♠ KJ72
♥ KJ5
♦ QJ42
♣ 75

West
♠ Q43
♥ A106
♦ 1098
♣ A864

East
♠ 9
♥ 9842
♦ 753
♣ QJ1032

South
♠ A10865
♥ Q73
♦ AK6
♣ K9

South	West	North	East
1♠	P	3♠[1]	P
4♠	All Pass		

1. Four card limit raise.

Lead: ♦10. Plan the play.

The threat is West holding the ♣A and East leading Clubs. Our focus should be on keeping East out of the lead before we discard a Club on our fourth Diamond. "Eight Ever, Nine Never." treats a suit in isolation. On this hand there is more to consider. Taking a finesse into West might seem right but if the finesse loses West could find the ♥A with East. Instead, use the Diamond suit after winning two rounds of trump. If the ♠Q falls, finish drawing trump and play Diamonds, discarding a Club. If the Queen does not appear start playing Diamonds, finishing in Dummy. If East has the remaining trump and has less than 3 Diamonds East will trump. You will go down if West has the ♣A. If West trumps an early Diamond you are safe as long as West also has the ♥A. This approach maximizes the number of things that can go right. How you start trump might be important. Win the opening lead in hand and lead up to the ♠K. That way you detect a 0–4 Spade split and can finesse East to avoid a trump loser.

Exercise 86

Vul: None; Dealer: East

North
- ♠ A943
- ♥ 4
- ♦ A976
- ♣ 9872

South
- ♠ KQJ1065
- ♥ 10753
- ♦ 5
- ♣ A4

East	South	West	North
1♥	1♠	2♥	3♥¹
4♥	4♠	5♥	5♠
All Pass			

1. Limit raise or better in Spades.

Lead: ♥2. East wins the ♥A and returns the ♣3. Plan the play.

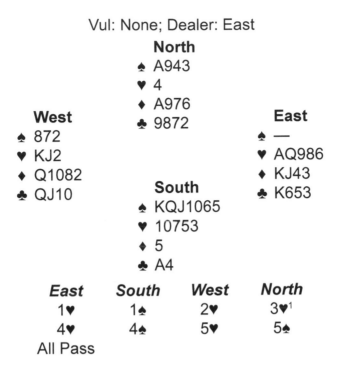

Vul: None; Dealer: East

North
♠ A943
♥ 4
♦ A976
♣ 9872

West
♠ 872
♥ KJ2
♦ Q1082
♣ QJ10

East
♠ —
♥ AQ986
♦ KJ43
♣ K653

South
♠ KQJ1065
♥ 10753
♦ 5
♣ A4

East	South	West	North
1♥	1♠	2♥	3♥[1]
4♥	4♠	5♥	5♠
All Pass			

1. Limit raise or better in Spades.

Lead: ♥2. East wins the ♥A and returns the ♣3. Plan the play.

With 2 Aces, 4 trumps and a valuable singleton North clearly has a limit raise. East's hand goes up in value knowing the Spade void is huge. South knows North can have at most 1 Heart (the opponents have 8) and South has a Diamond splinter. Even if trump are 2–1 South cannot make the hand by drawing trump. That approach will win 6 Spades in hand, 2 in Dummy plus the 2 minor suit Aces for 10. Fortunately Declarer has almost all of the high trumps so a high crossruff might work. South can see 3 Heart ruffs in Dummy (with no threat of an overruff), 6 Spades in hand and the ♦A and ♣A. South needs to pick the first two ruffs from hand carefully so that the ♠6 and ♠5 are not overruffed. Diamonds would have to be 6–2 for there to be a problem versus 5–2 for Clubs. Therefore Diamonds are safer given what South knows. South wins the ♣A, ruffs a Heart plays the ♦A and ruffs a Diamond low. South then ruffs another Heart, another Diamond high (since only 3 high Spades are needed to draw trump) and the last Heart. Declarer can now concede a Club trick and claim with a high cross ruff. This is not a 100% line of play because West could have one or zero Diamonds. It is the best play that South has for 5♠.

A Declarer's Workbook

Exercise 87

Vul: Both; Dealer: East

North
- ♠ K72
- ♥ 532
- ♦ 742
- ♣ KJ106

South
- ♠ AQ953
- ♥ QJ4
- ♦ AK3
- ♣ Q5

East	South	West	North
P	1♠	P	2♠
P	4♠	All Pass	

Lead: ♥7 to the East's ♥A. East returns the ♥8 to Declarer's ♥Q and West's ♥K. West exits with the ♥10 won by Declarer's ♥J. Now what?

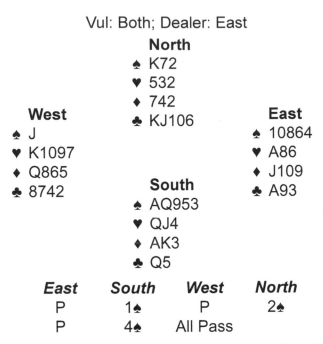

Vul: Both; Dealer: East

North
- ♠ K72
- ♥ 532
- ♦ 742
- ♣ KJ106

West
- ♠ J
- ♥ K1097
- ♦ Q865
- ♣ 8742

East
- ♠ 10864
- ♥ A86
- ♦ J109
- ♣ A93

South
- ♠ AQ953
- ♥ QJ4
- ♦ AK3
- ♣ Q5

East	South	West	North
P	1♠	P	2♠
P	4♠	All Pass	

Lead: ♥7 to the East's ♥A. East returns the ♥8 to Declarer's ♥Q and West's ♥K. West exits with the ♥10 won by Declarer's ♥J. Now what?

You have lost two tricks and have a quick loser in Clubs and a slow loser in Diamonds. Dummy's Clubs provide a resting place for your third Diamond but there is a trap. If you draw all of the trump how will you get to your good Clubs if West signals correctly so that East knows to take the second Club? The ♠K is your only Dummy entry so you must not draw all of the trump before forcing out the ♣A. If trump split 3–2 you could draw two rounds of trump, force out the ♣A and get to Dummy by drawing the last trump. What about a 4–1 trump split? There is only one 4–1 trump split you can survive: either the ♠J or ♠10 with West and all others with East. If that is the case your third trump lead must be Dummy's ♠2 to finesse your ♠9. After winning the ♥J play the ♠A and look for the ♠J or ♠10 from West. If neither appears play for 3–2 Spades by clearing the ♣A, winning any return and drawing trump with the ♠Q and ♠K in that order. Then pitch your losing Diamond on a Club and claim. If West played a Spade honor under the ♠A clear the ♣A, win any return and play to the ♠K disclosing the trump distribution. Play a third round of Clubs, dumping a Diamond. Then, if trump are 4–1 take the trump finesse and claim.

A Declarer's Workbook

Exercise 88

Vul: Both; Dealer: South

North
- ♠ KQ
- ♥ AK7
- ♦ AKJ43
- ♣ AKJ

South
- ♠ A4
- ♥ QJ10853
- ♦ 752
- ♣ 85

South	West	North	East
2♥	P	4NT¹	P
5♣²	P	5♦³	P
6♥⁴	P	7♥	All Pass

1. *RKC 1430.*
2. *One or four.*
3. *Queen ask.*
4. *Yes but no outside Kings.*

Lead: ♥2. Plan the play.

Vul: Both; Dealer: South

North
- ♠ KQ
- ♥ AK7
- ♦ AKJ43
- ♣ AKJ

West
- ♠ J8753
- ♥ 2
- ♦ 1096
- ♣ 9632

East
- ♠ 10962
- ♥ 964
- ♦ Q8
- ♣ Q1074

South
- ♠ A4
- ♥ QJ10853
- ♦ 752
- ♣ 85

South	West	North	East
2♥	P	4NT[1]	P
5♣[2]	P	5♦[3]	P
6♥[4]	P	7♥	All Pass

1. RKC 1430.
2. One or four.
3. Queen ask.
4. Yes but no outside Kings.

Lead: ♥2. Plan the play.

The Spade duplication leaves you with 12 tricks. If you rely solely on a minor suit finesse you have a 50% chance. Playing out your Hearts and Spades will not help. Both Opponents can tell that you are missing both minor suit Queens or you would claim. They will not pitch a minor suit card if it takes them below 3 cards. There is no sure line of play but you have a good chance by combining. You have 8 Diamonds and 5 Clubs. Clearly the chance of dropping a singleton or doubleton Q is better in Diamonds. Win the ♥A, finish drawing trump and play your ♦A and ♦K. If the lady appears thank the bridge gods and claim. If not, play the ♣A (in case the ♣Q is lonely, fat chance), come to your hand with the ♠A and take the Club finesse. If it wins you pitch your losing Diamond on the ♣K. Combining the attempt to drop the ♦Q with the Club finesse gives you two chances instead of one to make your grand slam.

A Declarer's Workbook

Exercise 89

Vul: Both; Dealer: East
Scoring: IMPs

North
- ♠ AQ963
- ♥ 6
- ♦ 742
- ♣ AK84

South
- ♠ J
- ♥ K854
- ♦ AKQ106
- ♣ 963

East	South	West	North
P	1♦	P	1♠
P	2♦	P	3♣
P	3NT	All Pass	

Lead: ♥3 (Fourth best lead). East plays the ♥J. Plan the play.

Vul: Both; Dealer: East; Scoring: IMPs

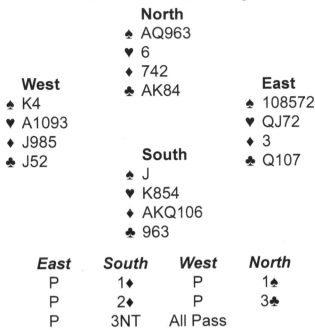

North
♠ AQ963
♥ 6
♦ 742
♣ AK84

West
♠ K4
♥ A1093
♦ J985
♣ J52

East
♠ 108572
♥ QJ72
♦ 3
♣ Q107

South
♠ J
♥ K854
♦ AKQ106
♣ 963

East	South	West	North
P	1♦	P	1♠
P	2♦	P	3♣
P	3NT	All Pass	

Lead: ♥3 (Fourth best lead). East plays the ♥J. Plan the play.

The location of the ♥2 tells whether West started with 4 or 5 Hearts but it does not appear on trick 1. If West started with 5 Hearts you cannot afford to lose the lead. You must win trick 1 because you cannot allow East to attack your ♥K. With 5 Diamond tricks you have 9 off the top. You score 5 Diamonds whenever they are 3–2, whenever East holds 4 (regardless of where the ♦J is) and whenever East holds the ♦J singleton. Attack Diamonds first because all other strategies risk losing the lead. What are you going to do if you learn on the second Diamond that West holds ♦Jxxx? You only have 7 top tricks but do not give up!! In your mind construct a lie of the cards that will allow you to succeed. You can score a trick with your fifth Diamond if you give West the ♦J. If West started with 5 Hearts you will be set but if West started with only 4 your fifth Diamond will get you to eight tricks. If the Spade finesse wins you make your contract. If Diamonds are 5–0 in either direction you have to hope that Hearts are 4–4. Defer playing more Diamonds and duck a Club. Win any return and hope for Clubs being 3–3 and the Spade finesse working. Do not surrender if the Diamonds fail!

A Declarer's Workbook

Exercise 90

Vul: Both; Dealer: South

North
- ♠ AQ87
- ♥ J52
- ♦ J72
- ♣ KQ5

South
- ♠ K9654
- ♥ KQ3
- ♦ KQ6
- ♣ 84

South	West	North	East
1♠	P	2NT¹	P
4♠²	All Pass		

1. Game Force with 4 card support.
2. Minimum opening hand; no shortness or slam interest.

Lead: ♣6. East wins your ♣K with the ♣A and returns the ♣2. Plan the play.

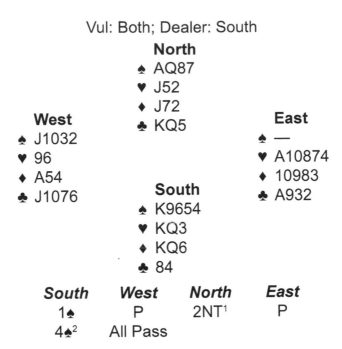

Vul: Both; Dealer: South

North
♠ AQ87
♥ J52
♦ J72
♣ KQ5

West
♠ J1032
♥ 96
♦ A54
♣ J1076

East
♠ —
♥ A10874
♦ 10983
♣ A932

South
♠ K9654
♥ KQ3
♦ KQ6
♣ 84

South	West	North	East
1♠	P	2NT¹	P
4♠²	All Pass		

1. Game Force with 4 card support.
2. Minimum opening hand; no shortness or slam interest.

Lead: ♣6. East wins your ♣K with the ♣A and returns the ♣2. Plan the play.

A comfortable auction has landed you in what looks easy. You have an unavoidable loser in each side suit. With the top 3 honors, bringing in the Spades without a loser looks simple. If you play the ♠A at trick 3 on this layout you will have set yourself by not considering your options. The only danger in Spades is a 4–0 split. If East holds 4 Spades the contract will fail because East's first Spade honor will force out the ♠K and East's second Spade honor will score. If West has 4 Spades you will be able to finesse twice, thereby capturing both Spade honors. The solution is to lead up to the ♠K at trick 3. This will disclose the 4–0 split and you will have two marked finesses against West. We presented a problem earlier where you held both the 10 and 9 of trump. In that case you could play one of Dummy's two high trump and take a single finesse in either direction. The lack of the ♠10 changes everything. The solution is easy once you see the problem. Ask yourself what can go wrong, looking closely at the spot cards. Careful planning often wins the hand!

Exercise 91

Vul: None; Dealer: East

North
- ♠ Q952
- ♥ 7542
- ♦ AK7
- ♣ 72

South
- ♠ AK10643
- ♥ 86
- ♦ J54
- ♣ AQ

East	South	West	North
P	1♠	P	3♠¹
P	4♠	All Pass	

1. *Limit raise with 4 trump.*

Lead: ♥A from AK. East encourages with the ♥Q. West continues with the ♥K and ♥9. Plan the play.

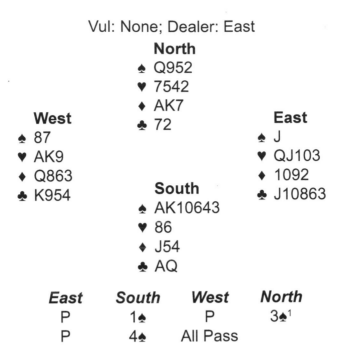

Vul: None; Dealer: East

North
♠ Q952
♥ 7542
♦ AK7
♣ 72

West
♠ 87
♥ AK9
♦ Q863
♣ K954

East
♠ J
♥ QJ103
♦ 1092
♣ J10863

South
♠ AK10643
♥ 86
♦ J54
♣ AQ

East	South	West	North
P	1♠	P	3♠[1]
P	4♠	All Pass	

1. Limit raise with 4 trump.

Lead: ♥A from AK. East encourages with the ♥Q. West continues with the ♥K and ♥9. Plan the play.

You have lost 2 Hearts and unless the ♦Q falls in 2 rounds you have a Diamond loser. Does everything depend on the Club finesse? You have a suit you want West to lead: Clubs. Is an end play possible? Draw trump and ruff Dummy's last Heart. Play the ♦A and ♦K. If the ♦Q does not fall, play your ♦J. If West holds the ♦Q West must take it and but will have no safe exit. If East wins the ♦Q the next lead will likely be a Club and you will be forced to fall back on the Club finesse. It is only 50/50 that West has the ♦Q but if that is the case, you have a guaranteed line of play. You have used a possible end play to combine your chances. You succeed if (1) the ♦Q falls in 2 rounds, (2) West holds the ♦Q or (3) East holds the ♣K. Astute readers will see that West can foil this strategy at trick 2 by leading away from the ♥K. East's ♥Q promises the ♥J or a singleton. If East then shifts to a Club rather than continuing Hearts you will be forced to try the Club finesse immediately. Sometimes we pay off to top notch defense. That is bridge!

Exercise 92

Vul: Both; Dealer: East

North
- ♠ 10974
- ♥ K854
- ♦ A96
- ♣ 84

South
- ♠ K5
- ♥ 76
- ♦ KQ873
- ♣ A632

East	South	West	North
P	1♦	P	1♥
P	2♣	P	2♦
All Pass			

Lead: ♥Q. Plan the play.

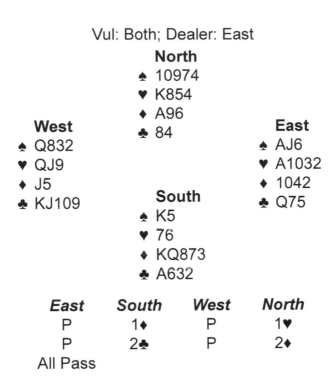

Vul: Both; Dealer: East

North
♠ 10974
♥ K854
♦ A96
♣ 84

West
♠ Q832
♥ QJ9
♦ J5
♣ KJ109

East
♠ AJ6
♥ A1032
♦ 1042
♣ Q75

South
♠ K5
♥ 76
♦ KQ873
♣ A632

East	South	West	North
P	1♦	P	1♥
P	2♣	P	2♦
All Pass			

Lead: ♥Q. Plan the play.

This hand will never be written up in a Daily Bulletin but it contains an opportunity that all good players will seize. The Opponents have the balance of power so you might content yourself with drawing trump to win 5 Diamond tricks, a Club and 0, 1 or 2 tricks in the majors depending on where the Aces lie. The problem with this approach is that at matchpoints your down 1 will likely earn you a bottom board and at teams you could turn a +90 into a −100 and lose 5 IMPs. On the ♥Q lead you should duck twice, ruff the third heart and lead a low Club (*not the ♣A*) to set up one or two Club ruffs in Dummy. Taking a trick or two with the ♦6 and ♦9 will pay big dividends! Depending on the defense and lie of the cards you might even be able to ruff two Clubs without trumping with the ♦A. On the layout shown you should score 1 Spade, 1 Club, a Club ruff in Dummy and the 5 Diamonds in your hand, thereby making your contract. Doing so will not make you famous but it will get you a good score. Partner will be happy and that is always a good thing!

Exercise 93

Vul: E/W; Dealer: East

North
- ♠ 9843
- ♥ AQ
- ♦ 863
- ♣ A1074

South
- ♠ A765
- ♥ 8742
- ♦ AKQ
- ♣ K5

East	South	West	North
P	1NT	P	2♣
P	2♥	P	3NT
P	4♠	All Pass	

Lead: ♦5. Plan the play.

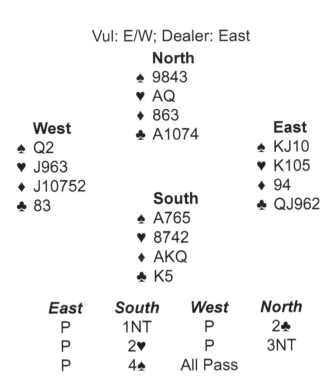

Vul: E/W; Dealer: East

North
♠ 9843
♥ AQ
♦ 863
♣ A1074

West
♠ Q2
♥ J963
♦ J10752
♣ 83

East
♠ KJ10
♥ K105
♦ 94
♣ QJ962

South
♠ A765
♥ 8742
♦ AKQ
♣ K5

East	South	West	North
P	1NT	P	2♣
P	2♥	P	3NT
P	4♠	All Pass	

Lead: ♦5. Plan the play.

You have no minor suit losers. You have a possible Heart loser and you must ruff 2 Hearts in Dummy. If trump are 3–2 you can hold your trump losers to 2 by ducking a trump, playing the Ace and leaving the high trump outstanding. That will leave 2 trumps in Dummy to ruff Hearts but there is a problem. Before you can ruff Hearts you have to take the Heart finesse. When should you take that finesse? If you draw two rounds of trump and then lose the Heart finesse to East a trump will be lead if East has another. This defense will draw one of Dummy's trumps that you were going to use to ruff Hearts. You can prevent this defense by taking the Heart finesse *before* drawing trumps. East cannot hurt you by playing trump if the finesse loses before your draw trump. You were planning on ducking a round of trump anyway. If the finesse loses and East leads a trump you duck, win any return, play the ♠A and play the ♥A. You then use Diamonds as entries to ruff the 2 low Hearts that are in your hand. The way to prevent East from drawing a third round of trump if the Heart finesse loses is by taking the Heart finesse *before* drawing trump.

A Declarer's Workbook

Exercise 94

Vul: N/S; Dealer: South

North
- ♠ —
- ♥ KQJ85
- ♦ Q873
- ♣ Q742

South
- ♠ A942
- ♥ A1093
- ♦ K42
- ♣ A8

South	West	North	East
1NT	P	2♦¹	P
2♥	P	3NT²	P
4♥	All Pass		

1. *Transfer.*
2. *Pass or Correct to 4♥.*

Lead: ♠K. Plan the play.

Vul: N/S; Dealer: South

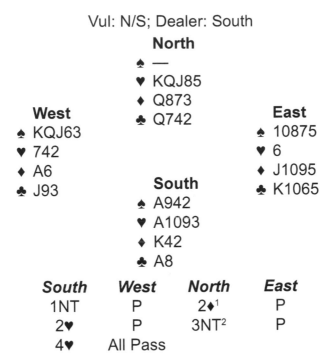

North
- ♠ —
- ♥ KQJ85
- ♦ Q873
- ♣ Q742

West
- ♠ KQJ63
- ♥ 742
- ♦ A6
- ♣ J93

East
- ♠ 10875
- ♥ 6
- ♦ J1095
- ♣ K1065

South
- ♠ A942
- ♥ A1093
- ♦ K42
- ♣ A8

South	West	North	East
1NT	P	2♦¹	P
2♥	P	3NT²	P
4♥	All Pass		

1. Transfer.   *2. Pass or Correct to 4♥.*

Lead: ♠K. Plan the play.

If trump are 2–2 this hand is easy. If trump are 3–1 you have a problem. If you draw 3 rounds of trump to start you will likely be left with a losing Spade. Instead use an almost 100% path. You have plenty of high trump so execute a Dummy Reversal in order to ruff 3 Spades in Dummy before drawing the last trump. You can do this while testing trump. You have limited entries to hand outside of trump so careful planning is necessary. Ruff the opening lead,thereby saving an entry. Return to hand with the ♣A and lead up to the ♣Q. If West has the ♣K you will have created a resting spot for your ♦2 and make an overtrick. After losing to the ♣K return to hand twice with the ♥10 and ♥A to ruff your remaining small Spades. If the Club finesse established the ♣Q you should play it after the second Spade ruff to discard the ♦2. If trump were 2–2 you can claim either 10 or 11 tricks depending on whether the ♣Q was a winner. If trump were 3–1 you can return to hand by ruffing a Club or a Diamond to draw the last trump and claim either 10 or 11 tricks. If you play two rounds of trump early in hope of a 2–2 split you will not have sufficient entries to execute the Dummy Reversal. If trump are 3–1 (the most likely split) your contract will fail.

Exercise 95

Vul: Both; Dealer: West

North
- ♠ 862
- ♥ KJ5
- ♦ A74
- ♣ AK84

South
- ♠ 9
- ♥ AQ108
- ♦ K862
- ♣ QJ76

West	North	East	South
1♠	X	3♠[1]	4♥
All Pass			

1. Preemptive.

Lead: ♠A followed by ♠Q. Plan the play.

Vul: Both; Dealer: West

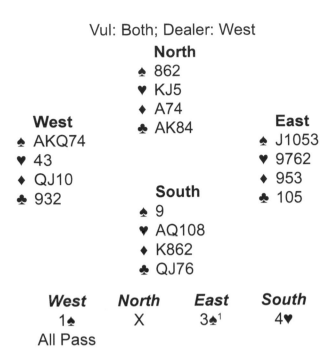

North
- ♠ 862
- ♥ KJ5
- ♦ A74
- ♣ AK84

West
- ♠ AKQ74
- ♥ 43
- ♦ QJ10
- ♣ 932

East
- ♠ J1053
- ♥ 9762
- ♦ 953
- ♣ 105

South
- ♠ 9
- ♥ AQ108
- ♦ K862
- ♣ QJ76

West	*North*	*East*	*South*
1♠	X	3♠[1]	4♥
All Pass			

1. Preemptive.

Lead: ♠A followed by ♠Q. Plan the play.

You have 1 Spade loser and 2 possible Diamond losers. If you avoid a trump loser and draw all the trump you can win 4 Hearts, 2 Diamonds and 4 Clubs. If you ruff the ♠Q you will shorten South's trump length to 3. If trump split 4–2 ruffing in hand will create a trump loser. You do not have to hope trump are 3–3. There is a better plan. Notice that ruffing the fourth Spade in Dummy would leave South's hand with 4 trump. Instead of ruffing West's second and third Spades in hand you should discard a losing Diamond on each. If West continues Spades after winning 3 Spade tricks you can ruff high in Dummy. If West makes any other lead, win it. Now draw trump. If Hearts are no worse than 4–2 you will succeed. All your game contracts should be this good!! Pitching Diamonds instead of ruffing in the South hand is a **loser-on-loser play**. You preserve South's four card trump holding while exchanging two Diamond losers for two Spade losers. A loser-on-loser play can often be used to preserve a hand's trump holding. This can allow you to avoid ruffing with trump you might need to draw the Opponents' trump.

A Declarer's Workbook

Exercise 96

Vul: Both; Dealer: South

North
- ♠ Q943
- ♥ A743
- ♦ Q3
- ♣ Q82

South
- ♠ A62
- ♥ K6
- ♦ A106
- ♣ KJ1074

South	West	North	East
1NT	P	2♣	P
2♦	P	3NT	All Pass

Lead: ♦7 (fourth best leads). Plan the play.

Vul: Both; Dealer: South

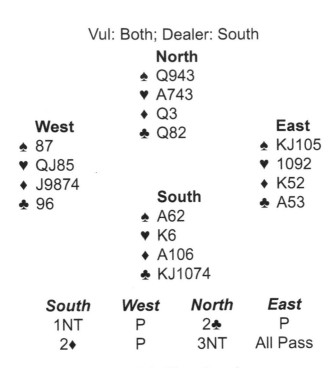

North
- ♠ Q943
- ♥ A743
- ♦ Q3
- ♣ Q82

West
- ♠ 87
- ♥ QJ85
- ♦ J9874
- ♣ 96

East
- ♠ KJ105
- ♥ 1092
- ♦ K52
- ♣ A53

South
- ♠ A62
- ♥ K6
- ♦ A106
- ♣ KJ1074

South	West	North	East
1NT	P	2♣	P
2♦	P	3NT	All Pass

Lead: ♦7 (fourth best leads). Plan the play.

You are going to have to drive out the ♣A to make this contract but if you only have 1 Diamond stopper and Diamonds are 5–3 or 6–2 this could be a problem. The Rule of 11 tells you that West has 3 Diamonds larger than the ♦7 while East has only 1 so it looks like the ♦K is more likely with West. We have danced this dance before but this time there is a big difference. Now you have the ♦10 in your hand and that changes everything. *No guess about playing the ♦Q is required.* If you duck in Dummy you are guaranteed 2 Diamond tricks. If East plays the ♦K you win the ♦A and your ♦Q is good. If East plays the ♦J then you win the ♦A and your ♦Q or ♦10 will win a trick later. Now you have time to drive out the ♣A and score 4 Clubs, 2 Diamonds, 2 Hearts and a Spade. You can finish by leading up to the ♠Q and perhaps score a tenth trick, but not on this layout. Remember this Diamond holding along with its brother Jx opposite A10x. If the lead of the suit comes from your left they cannot keep you from taking 2 tricks if you remember to duck the first lead in Dummy.

Exercise 97

Vul: Both; Dealer: West

North
- ♠ K1042
- ♥ 85
- ♦ AQ2
- ♣ A1094

South
- ♠ AJ953
- ♥ A4
- ♦ J64
- ♣ K32

West	North	East	South
P	1♣	P	1♠
P	2♠	P	4♠
All Pass			

Lead: ♥K. Plan the play.

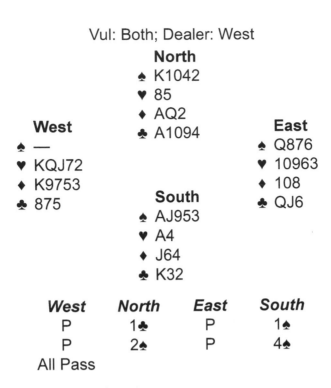

Vul: Both; Dealer: West

North
- ♠ K1042
- ♥ 85
- ♦ AQ2
- ♣ A1094

West
- ♠ —
- ♥ KQJ72
- ♦ K9753
- ♣ 875

East
- ♠ Q876
- ♥ 10963
- ♦ 108
- ♣ QJ6

South
- ♠ AJ953
- ♥ A4
- ♦ J64
- ♣ K32

West	North	East	South
P	1♣	P	1♠
P	2♠	P	4♠
All Pass			

Lead: ♥K. Plan the play.

This is a familiar situation. You have three losers so you must find the ♠Q. You have learned by now that with no knowledge of the Opponents' cards or one hand being more dangerous than the other that "Eight Ever, Nine Never" applies. With nine Spades you should play for the drop by winning the ♥A and taking two Spade tricks with the Ace and King. This is a no-brainer, right? ***Do not ever think like that.*** Have you thought about a possible though unlikely 4–0 split in Spades? With the spots you hold you can survive a 4–0 split in either direction if you lead low to the ♠A or ♠K. The problem is knowing which one. With the information available you have no clue. Less experienced players might give things away with body language but good players never do. This is a guess but there is one clever play that might simplify things. Win the ♥A and lead the ♥4 right back. Look at West's hand in the layout above. After winning the ♥Q any lead could cost a trick. If West happens to have a singleton small trump that might be the card played. Give the Opponents a chance to help you. If you have to guess, so be it but first give the Opponents a chance to solve your problem for you.

Exercise 98

Vul: Both; Dealer: East
Scoring: Matchpoints

North
- ♠ AQ963
- ♥ 6
- ♦ 742
- ♣ AK84

South
- ♠ J
- ♥ K854
- ♦ AKQ106
- ♣ 963

East	South	West	North
P	1♦	P	1♠
P	2♦	P	3♣
P	3NT	All Pass	

Lead: ♥3 (Fourth best lead). East plays the ♥J. Plan the play.

Vul: Both; Dealer: East; Scoring: Matchpoints

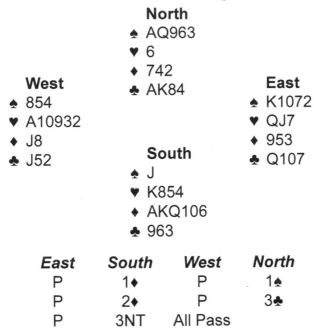

North
- ♠ AQ963
- ♥ 6
- ♦ 742
- ♣ AK84

West
- ♠ 854
- ♥ A10932
- ♦ J8
- ♣ J52

East
- ♠ K1072
- ♥ QJ7
- ♦ 953
- ♣ Q107

South
- ♠ J
- ♥ K854
- ♦ AKQ106
- ♣ 963

East	South	West	North
P	1♦	P	1♠
P	2♦	P	3♣
P	3NT	All Pass	

Lead: ♥3 (Fourth best lead). East plays the ♥J. Plan the play.

The North/South hands appeared earlier playing IMPs. The early play is the same for Matchpoints: win trick 1 and test the Diamonds. If both Opponents follow to the first 2 Diamonds you have 9 tricks – 1 Spade, 1 Heart 5 Diamonds and 2 Clubs. There is a tenth trick available by taking the Spade finesse but this risks your contract. This appears to be a 50/50 proposition but maybe you can learn something by playing out your Diamonds. The Opponents have two suits to guard: Spades and Clubs. They do not know you have a stiff Spade so the player with the ♠K will guard it. The other Opponent will likely pitch a Spade or two. They also do not know that you have seven Clubs. One of the Opponents might pitch a couple of Clubs from four small. Your Clubs could then set up with the ♣AK. The lesson here is that it often pays dividends, particularly at No Trump, to run your winners and watch the Opponents' discards like a hawk. You might learn something that will give you an overtrick or two. At Matchpoints that can get you a top board. On this hand, unless you get a clear indication from the discards that West has the ♠K most experts would avoid the Spade finesse even at matchpoints.

A Declarer's Workbook

Exercise 99

Vul: Both; Dealer: South

North
- ♠ KQ43
- ♥ 985
- ♦ J1052
- ♣ A6

South
- ♠ J752
- ♥ AK6
- ♦ AQ63
- ♣ K9

South	West	North	East
1NT	P	2♣	P
2♠	P	4♠	All Pass

Lead: ♣Q. Plan the play.

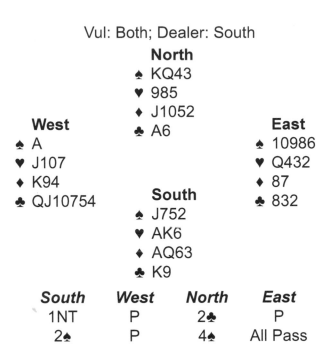

Vul: Both; Dealer: South

North
♠ KQ43
♥ 985
♦ J1052
♣ A6

West
♠ A
♥ J107
♦ K94
♣ QJ10754

East
♠ 10986
♥ Q432
♦ 87
♣ 832

South
♠ J752
♥ AK6
♦ AQ63
♣ K9

South	West	North	East
1NT	P	2♣	P
2♠	P	4♠	All Pass

Lead: ♣Q. Plan the play.

This looks easy. There is 1 loser each in Spades and Hearts and a possible loser in Diamonds. If trumps are 3–2 you can play the K, Q and J to draw trump. The Diamond finesse will be for an overtrick and you can take it if you finish drawing trump in Dummy. What if trump are 4–1 and the Diamond finesse loses? If the defender holding the ♠A leads a second Club the suit will be wide open. If you draw trump and lose the Diamond finesse the Opponents will be able to run Clubs. Therefore you must take the Diamond finesse before you finish drawing trump. Additionally, you must start Spades by leading a low Spade up to an honor rather than leading an honor. Hopefully a singleton ♠A will fall on air. Preserve the ♣A to get to Dummy to take the Diamond finesse after driving out the ♠A. Win the ♣K and lead the ♠2. If a singleton ♠A appears you have 3 top Spades to draw trump. West will return a Club. Win the ♣A *but do not draw trump yet*. Since you can afford to lose 1 Diamond trick lead the ♦J intending to finesse unless East plays the ♦K. You will score an overtrick whenever East holds the ♦Kx(x) and lose a Diamond otherwise. If the finesse loses, draw trump immediately upon regaining the lead. If East has the singleton ♦K win it and draw trump. You will eventually lose a Diamond but not before winning 3 Spades, 2 Hearts, 3 Diamonds and 2 Clubs. Unless East has the singleton ♠A or Spades are 5–0 you will lose 1 Spade, 1 Heart and 1 Diamond but no Clubs.

A Declarer's Workbook

Exercise 100

Vul: N/S; Dealer: North

North
- ♠ 1075
- ♥ —
- ♦ AK83
- ♣ K108742

South
- ♠ AKJ94
- ♥ J432
- ♦ J754
- ♣ —

North	East	South	West
1♣	1♥	1♠	P
2♠	3♥	3♠	All Pass

Lead: ♥K. Plan the play.

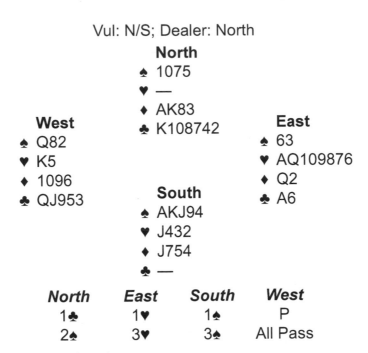

Vul: N/S; Dealer: North

North
♠ 1075
♥ —
♦ AK83
♣ K108742

West
♠ Q82
♥ K5
♦ 1096
♣ QJ953

East
♠ 63
♥ AQ109876
♦ Q2
♣ A6

South
♠ AKJ94
♥ J432
♦ J754
♣ —

North	East	South	West
1♣	1♥	1♠	P
2♠	3♥	3♠	All Pass

Lead: ♥K. Plan the play.

This is a crossruff hand if ever there was one but there are some important plays that need to be made by each side. What should South do after ruffing the ♥K in dummy? If Declarer starts right in on the crossruff something bad is going to happen when South tries to cash Dummy's ♦AK. East can discard Diamonds when Clubs are being ruffed and West can pitch Diamonds when Hearts are being ruffed. There is an easy remedy for South that applies to crossruff hands almost all the time. *Take your outside winners before starting the crossruff.* After ruffing the ♥K South calls for Dummy's ♦AK and then starts the crossruff. The next important decision comes to West. When the third Heart is led West must rise with the ♠Q and lead a trump right back. Otherwise Declarer will score 3 Spades in Dummy, 5 in hand plus 2 Diamonds for 10 tricks. By rising with the ♠Q and leading a trump West crushes one of Dummy's trumps, thereby holding Declarer to 9 tricks. At IMPs this play saves 1 IMP. At Matchpoints this play could be the difference between a bottom board and a good one. When defending against a crossruff it is almost always right to lead trump as soon as you can and at every opportunity. On this hand West cannot know to lead trump at trick 1 but after seeing Dummy it should be clear to rise with the ♠Q as soon as possible and lead trump.

A Declarer's Workbook

Exercise 101

Vul: E/W; Dealer: South

North
♠ 843
♥ KJ1063
♦ 7
♣ Q864

South
♠ KQ97
♥ 87
♦ Q95
♣ AK95

South	West	North	East
1♣	P	1♥	P
1♠	P	2♣	2♦
P	P	3♣	All Pass

Lead: ♦A (A from AK). East's ♦2 shows Heart values. Not wanting to set up Dummy's Hearts, West leads the ♣J. Plan the play.

Vul: E/W; Dealer: South

North
- ♠ 843
- ♥ KJ1063
- ♦ 7
- ♣ Q864

West
- ♠ J1052
- ♥ 954
- ♦ AK84
- ♣ J2

East
- ♠ A6
- ♥ AQ2
- ♦ J10632
- ♣ 1073

South
- ♠ KQ97
- ♥ 87
- ♦ Q95
- ♣ AK95

South	West	North	East
1♣	P	1♥	P
1♠	P	2♣	2♦
P	P	3♣	All Pass

Lead: ♦A (A from AK). East's ♦2 shows Heart values. Not wanting to set up Dummy's Hearts, West leads the ♣J. Plan the play.

Is ruffing two Diamonds best? Getting to hand for the second Diamond ruff is problematic. Consider what the auction says about the distribution. You were allowed to play 3♣ so it is unlikely that either defender has a 6 card or longer suit. Clubs are probably 3–2 since neither opponent made a takeout double. If that is so you have two Dummy entries: the ♣Q and the fourth Club. Notice also that West did not lead a Heart after East showed Heart values (the ♥AQ). With either a singleton or doubleton West would surely have lead a Heart hoping to ruff a Heart. Since Hearts are likely splitting 3–3 why not establish Hearts instead of ruffing Diamonds? Start by winning the ♣A and take the losing Heart finesse. If a Diamond comes back, ruff it and play the ♥K to establish the ♥10. If a Club comes back, win it in hand and lead a Heart to establish the ♥10. You win any return and use your three good Hearts to pitch two Spades and a Diamond after drawing trump. There are a couple of lessons here. (1) Use the Opponents' bids and defensive signals to discern their shape and (2) always consider a meaty five card side suit as a potential source of tricks.

A Declarer's Workbook

Exercise 102

Vul: Both; Dealer: East

North
- ♠ 93
- ♥ AK743
- ♦ 842
- ♣ AQ9

South
- ♠ A1087542
- ♥ 6
- ♦ A73
- ♣ 84

East	South	West	North
P	3♠	P	4♠
All Pass			

Lead: ♦K. Plan the play.

Vul: Both; Dealer: East

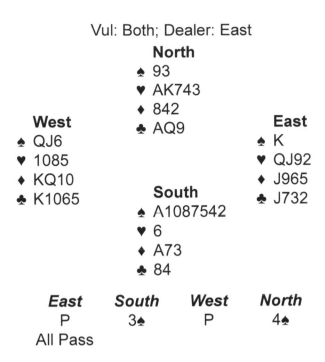

North
- ♠ 93
- ♥ AK743
- ♦ 842
- ♣ AQ9

West
- ♠ QJ6
- ♥ 1085
- ♦ KQ10
- ♣ K1065

East
- ♠ K
- ♥ QJ92
- ♦ J965
- ♣ J732

South
- ♠ A1087542
- ♥ 6
- ♦ A73
- ♣ 84

East	South	West	North
P	3♠	P	4♠
All Pass			

Lead: ♦K. Plan the play.

This is not a hard hand for declarers who make a plan before play-ing to the first trick. In a suit contract start by counting your losers. You have 1 or 2 in Spades unless there is a 4–0 split to your left. You have a possible Club loser plus 2 in Diamonds. Without the ♦K lead you could have drawn trump before pitching a Diamond but the lead turned those 2 small Diamonds into fast losers – the Oppo-nents will cash them as soon as they get in – and they are surely getting in when you draw trump. The ♥AK provides a resting spot for one of Declarer's Diamonds but you have to play them before drawing trump. You would prefer to draw trump first but the open-ing lead makes that impossible. When the Hearts hold you hope for 2–2 Spades but are disappointed. You have 2 Spade losers and a Diamond loser. As the cards lie the Club finesse is on so you make a nice 4 Spade contract. When you have fast losers such as the two small Diamonds and an obvious place to discard one or both of them you must postpone drawing trump if there is a risk that you will lose the lead.

Exercise 103

Vul: None; Dealer: East

North
- ♠ K95
- ♥ K53
- ♦ A642
- ♣ AQ6

South
- ♠ A1086432
- ♥ A8
- ♦ K9
- ♣ 83

East	South	West	North
P	1♠	P	2♦¹
P	2♠	P	3♠²
P	4♦³	P	4♥³
P	4NT⁴	P	5♦⁵
P	6♠	All Pass	

1. Game forcing.
2. Slam interest, please cue bid.
3. Control showing.
4. RKC 1430
5.Zero or 3 Key Cards.

Lead: ♥Q. You win the ♥A and lead the ♠2. West discards the ♥2 (standard signals). What now?

Vul: None; Dealer: East

North
♠ K95
♥ K53
♦ A642
♣ AQ6

West
♠ —
♥ QJ1072
♦ Q1073
♣ J952

East
♠ QJ7
♥ 964
♦ J85
♣ K1074

South
♠ A1086432
♥ A8
♦ K9
♣ 83

East	South	West	North
P	1♠	P	2♦¹
P	2♠	P	3♠²
P	4♦³	P	4♥³
P	4NT⁴	P	5♦⁵
P	6♠	All Pass	

1. Game forcing.
2. Slam interest, please cue bid.
3. Control showing.
4. RKC 1430
5. Zero or 3 Key Cards.

Lead: ♥Q. You win the ♥A and lead the ♠2. West discards the ♥2 (standard signals). What now?

You have a trump loser. Does your slam depend on the Club finesse? You can use East's winning trump as a throw-in card but you do not have enough trump in Dummy to create a ruff and sluff position. Is there a lie of the cards that will let you put East on lead with nothing but Clubs? East has 3 Spades. If East also has only 3 Hearts and 3 Diamonds you can play out these suits and put East on lead with a trump. East will hold nothing but Clubs. It costs nothing to win the ♠K and ♠A and play 3 rounds each of Hearts and Diamonds. If East has a 4 card or longer red suit East will lead a red card after winning the trump trick. You will have no choice but to fall back on the Club finesse. If East has the distribution you desire, the Club problem disappears. You also succeed if East has less than 3 cards in a red suit if you guess to play the other red suit first – not that there is any way for you to know. This approach combines chances by trying for the end play and taking the Club finesse if the end play fails.

A Declarer's Workbook

Exercise 104

Vul: E/W; Dealer: West

North
- ♠ AQJ
- ♥ 8754
- ♦ K52
- ♣ K76

South
- ♠ K7542
- ♥ 9
- ♦ A74
- ♣ A852

West	North	East	South
P	1♣	P	1♠
P	1NT	P	2♦¹
P	2♠²	P	4♠
All Pass			

1. Do you have 3 Spades?
2. Yes.

Lead: ♦Q. Plan the play.

Vul: E/W; Dealer: West

North
- ♠ AQJ
- ♥ 8754
- ♦ K52
- ♣ K76

West
- ♠ 6
- ♥ KJ103
- ♦ QJ1093
- ♣ J103

East
- ♠ 10983
- ♥ AQ62
- ♦ 86
- ♣ Q94

South
- ♠ K7542
- ♥ 9
- ♦ A74
- ♣ A852

West	North	East	South
P	1♣	P	1♠
P	1NT	P	2♦¹
P	2♠²	P	4♠
All Pass			

1. Do you have 3 Spades?
2. Yes.

Lead: ♦Q. Plan the play.

If either Opponent has a singleton Club or Diamond or two or fewer Hearts, you can be set. Ignore those possibilities and use a Dummy Reversal. Win trick 1 with the ♦A and lead a low Heart. If they return a Heart, ruff it. Win any other return in Dummy. One Spade and the minor suit Kings provide the 3 entries to Dummy needed to ruff 3 Hearts in hand. Assume West wins the ♥K and returns a Diamond (as good a defense as any). Win the ♦K and ruff a Heart. Return to Dummy twice with the ♠A and ♣K to ruff two more Hearts, using the ♠K if East ruffs high. You will have won three Spades in Dummy, three Heart ruffs in hand plus the top two honors in each of the minors for a total of 10 tricks. The only other approach is to establish your fourth Club on a 3–3 split or ruff your fourth Club in Dummy. That requires delaying drawing trump. The Dummy Reversal is the safer approach.

A Declarer's Workbook

Exercise 105

Vul: E/W; Dealer: East
Matchpoints

North
♠ —
♥ J1072
♦ 10986
♣ AK983

South
♠ KQ7
♥ AQ853
♦ A4
♣ 764

East	South	West	North
2♠	2NT	P	3♣¹
P	3♥	P	4♥
All Pass			

1. Stayman

Lead: ♠10. Plan the play.

Vul: E/W; Dealer: East; Matchpoints

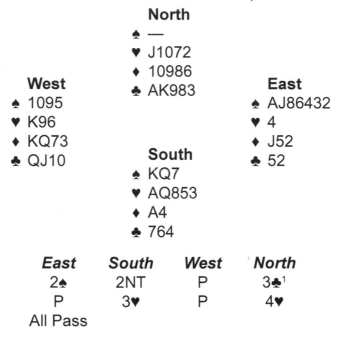

North
- ♠ —
- ♥ J1072
- ♦ 10986
- ♣ AK983

West
- ♠ 1095
- ♥ K96
- ♦ KQ73
- ♣ QJ10

East
- ♠ AJ86432
- ♥ 4
- ♦ J52
- ♣ 52

South
- ♠ KQ7
- ♥ AQ853
- ♦ A4
- ♣ 764

East	South	West	North
2♠	2NT	P	3♣¹
P	3♥	P	4♥
All Pass			

1. Stayman

Lead: ♠10. Plan the play.

Your first impulse might be to ruff the opening lead. Surely East has the ♠A so you will still have a Spade loser. You also have certain losers in Clubs and Diamonds and a possible trump loser. How can you guarantee your contract even if the trump finesse fails? What will happen if you play a small Diamond on the ♠10? East must win the ♠A or you will win the ♠K and ruff the remaining Spades, thereby eliminating a Spade loser. When East plays the ♠A your ♠K and ♠Q are established as resting places for two more Diamonds. Dummy's fourth Diamond goes under your ♦A. Your Diamond loser just disappeared. What you have done is play a Diamond loser from Dummy on a Spade loser in hand, thereby eliminating a loser – a classic loser-on-loser play. By pitching a Diamond on trick 1 instead of ruffing you guarantee your contract and will make an overtrick if the Heart finesse wins. You have a void opposite the second and third ranked Spades. When West correctly leads East's suit you are offered a gift. Be smart enough to take it! Only the observant declarers will do so.

Exercise 106

Vul: Both; Dealer: West

North
- ♠ A76
- ♥ K642
- ♦ J943
- ♣ A6

South
- ♠ K84
- ♥ Q853
- ♦ AQ107
- ♣ K3

West	North	East	South
P	1♦	P	1♥
P	2♥	P	4♥
All Pass			

Lead: ♣Q. Plan the play.

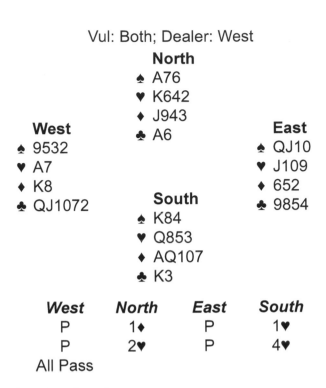

Vul: Both; Dealer: West

North
- ♠ A76
- ♥ K642
- ♦ J943
- ♣ A6

West
- ♠ 9532
- ♥ A7
- ♦ K8
- ♣ QJ1072

East
- ♠ QJ10
- ♥ J109
- ♦ 652
- ♣ 9854

South
- ♠ K84
- ♥ Q853
- ♦ AQ107
- ♣ K3

West	North	East	South
P	1♦	P	1♥
P	2♥	P	4♥
All Pass			

Lead: ♣Q. Plan the play.

You have a Spade loser, a possible Diamond loser and 1 or 2 trump losers. Preserve a Dummy entry for the Diamond finesses. If that finesse loses your contract will depend on losing only 1 trump. We have previously addressed the problem of Kxxx facing Qxxx. We know to lead up to one of the trump honors, hoping that we are leading through the Ace. If we are successful we then duck a round of trump, hoping that the Ace was doubleton. How do you know which trump honor to lead up to? Sometimes the bidding helps, but not here. If you know nothing about the location of the opponents' strength attempt to locate the doubleton and hope that it contains the Ace. The ♣Q lead is probably the top of a sequence. Hope that it is a 5 card or longer suit (making West the more likely to be short in Hearts) and lead up to the ♥K. You need to be lucky twice: first that you are leading through the ♥A and second that the Ace was double-ton. If the ♥K wins, lead a Heart back to your hand and *duck*. If this strategy fails you still have the Diamond finesse.

Exercise 107

Vul: N/S; Dealer: East

North
♠ 92
♥ K75
♦ KJ106
♣ K1062

South
♠ 854
♥ AQ6
♦ A32
♣ AJ74

East	*South*	*West*	*North*
P	1NT	P	3NT
All Pass			

Lead: ♠Q. The opponents take 4 Spade tricks – thankfully they are 4–4. East shifts to the ♥10. Plan the play.

Vul: N/S; Dealer: East

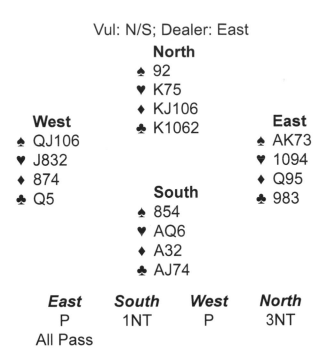

North
- ♠ 92
- ♥ K75
- ♦ KJ106
- ♣ K1062

West
- ♠ QJ106
- ♥ J832
- ♦ 874
- ♣ Q5

East
- ♠ AK73
- ♥ 1094
- ♦ Q95
- ♣ 983

South
- ♠ 854
- ♥ AQ6
- ♦ A32
- ♣ AJ74

East	*South*	*West*	*North*
P	1NT	P	3NT
All Pass			

Lead: ♠Q. The opponents take 4 Spade tricks – thankfully they are 4–4. East shifts to the ♥10. Plan the play.

You need the remaining 9 tricks. You have 7 off the top with two possible sources for tricks 8 and 9. You can finesse twice in Diamonds and that will give you two more tricks if the ♦Q is right. The other choice is Clubs where you need the ♣Q onside (whichever side that might be) and a 3–2 Club break since you lack the ♣9. That is not as likely to work as the Diamond finesse so it appears that your best bet is Diamonds. You could also try to drop the ♣Q by playing the ♣K followed by the ♣A. The ♣Q will sometimes drop. That appears to be an inferior play but notice that you can try that approach without losing the lead. If the ♣Q falls on the table your contract is safe. If not, you can fall back on the double finesse in Diamonds. This is a "combining" hand if ever there was one because you can try to drop the ♣Q without the risk of losing the lead. Two chances are always better than one if you can hold onto the lead.

Exercise 108

Vul: E/W; Dealer: North

North
- ♠ 982
- ♥ 94
- ♦ AKJ102
- ♣ Q84

South
- ♠ AK43
- ♥ A82
- ♦ 743
- ♣ A32

North	*East*	*South*	*West*
P	P	1NT	P
3NT	All Pass		

Lead: ♣6. Plan the play.

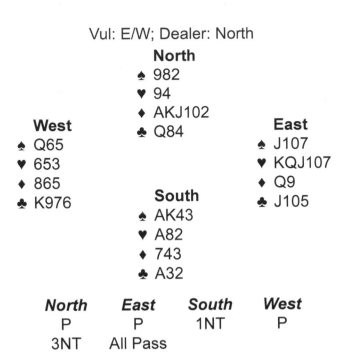

Vul: E/W; Dealer: North

North
♠ 982
♥ 94
♦ AKJ102
♣ Q84

West
♠ Q65
♥ 653
♦ 865
♣ K976

East
♠ J107
♥ KQJ107
♦ Q9
♣ J105

South
♠ AK43
♥ A82
♦ 743
♣ A32

North	East	South	West
P	P	1NT	P
3NT	All Pass		

Lead: ♣6. Plan the play.

West found a weak spot. You might only have 1 Club stopper. If so and if the Diamond finesse loses then you are going to be set when Clubs are 5–2 or worse. Should you play the ♣Q? If West led fourth best then the Rule of 11 says that East has only two Clubs higher than the ♣6 while West has 3. So the odds appear to be 3 to 2 that West has the ♣K but there is more to consider than Clubs. You have only one Heart stopper and the Opponents have eight Hearts. If you play the ♣4 on trick one East will force your ♣A. If the Diamond finesse wins you can take nine tricks and a possible tenth by leading up to the ♣Q. But if the finesse loses East will not lead a Club because that would establish Dummy's ♣Q as the ninth trick. Instead East will shift to a Heart and the Opponents will drive out your ♥A. You would still need to drive out the ♣K to take nine tricks and whoever wins that ♣K will be able to shift to Hearts and set you. You need one of two things to happen: either the ♣K or the ♦Q has to be with West. Do not let the Opponents attack Hearts. There is no guarantee that the ♣6 is fourth best. It might be from ♣K96 and East is long in Clubs. You must play the ♣Q at trick one because it takes advantage of one of the two chances you have to make your contract.

A Declarer's Workbook